The
Secret
Addiction

OVERCOMING YOUR MARIJUANA DEPENDENCY

DR. TONY DeRAMUS

The Secret Addiction: Overcoming Your Marijuana Dependency

Copyright © 2021 by Tony W. DeRamus

Print ISBN: 978-0-9971941-8-0
eBook ISBN: 978-0-9971941-9-7

For information address:
SMA International, LLC
123 Blue Heron Dr., Ste 104
Montgomery, Texas 77316

For additional resources on overcoming marijuana addiction,
visit www.secretaddiction.org

Designed by The Dock Line, Inc.
www.thedockline.com

Contents

List of Personal Tasks

Dedication

Every time I pick up a book, I make sure that I read the dedication page. Whether it is short and to the point, or whether it covers the entire page, I read it. I suppose I'm just curious as to the important people in the author's life, and those who were instrumental in bringing the author's work to fruition.

Now, it's my turn. Without the people listed below, I would not have the honor of recognizing them on this page.

Oddly enough, I want to thank the couple who began growing marijuana in their house, and who so graciously allowed me to purchase a bag of their first crop! Without you, my miserable struggles and incongruences would have never happened. Without you, I would have never have felt the need to undertake such an enormous project, and without you I would never have had the opportunity to help so many others navigate a better path in life.

My thanks to all of you who took the time out of your busy schedules to read, critique, and provide commentary about this book. Each one of you has touched my life in a significant way!

Dr. Larry, you are like a father to me in many ways. You confront me when I am wrong, console me when I am down, and applaud me when I succeed. General Halstead, or Becky, you are such an inspiration. You are living proof that the mind is the most important component to success. And finally, Dr. Jim. You so willingly offered to read my book and provide commentary, knowing how significant that would be to a rookie author. You teach so many people how to remove "their story" from their lives in order to become an authentic person. Thank you for being that authentic person and allowing us to believe in what you teach.

In case I never write another book, thank you Mom and Dad. Every parent has the opportunity to mold a child in their own unique way. I would not be who I am today without you.

My two beautiful sons will never know how much their presence pushed me toward the person I am today. By default, they inspired me to become the bearer of a great responsibility, that of a father and a role model. I will continue to serve you two with a selfless heart.

My beautiful wife, you endured the years of selfishness and the agony of witnessing an individual trade his ambitions and talents for the complacent satisfaction of mere mediocrity. I am not sure how you managed to maintain even an ounce of respect for me, but you did. I love and appreciate you for that.

Finally, thank you, God. You helped put all the pieces together for our little undertaking. Through all of the silent nudging, it is finally complete.

Introduction

So lay claim to your greatness. Drive a stake into the
ground to mark your place under the sun. Stop being a
prisoner of your past and become the architect of your
future. And remember, it's never too late to become
the person you have always dreamed of becoming.

ROBIN SHARMA, *The Greatness Guide*

SEPTEMBER 22, 2006

So, here I am sitting on a plane for Dallas. It is 6:00 a.m. and for
some reason I have a feeling that what I am about to undertake
will be the most important thing I will ever do in my life. I am
certain there will be other very important tasks, but this project
is one, not only from a passionate perspective, but one out of
necessity. You see, the last seven years of my life have been pretty
much a blur. It has been seven years filled with much despair,
guilt, and stagnation.

The reason I feel this is necessary is not only to rescue others
from this experience, but to save myself as well. Before I started
to write, I prayed. I prayed that God will use me as an instrument
to give to you what I have needed for so long—hope. If I could
only be so fortunate to work with this higher power, as a partner,

to express the truth behind this secret addiction. So I pray to you again, God, to work through me, guide me, and encourage me. Provide me with the hope, so I will have the courage to escape my fears and complete the task you have placed before me.

It has been five days since I have last sat in my smoking refuge and got "high." Will this time be any different? For some reason, I think it might. But, then again, this is something I have uttered unsuccessfully on numerous occasions in the past. Mark Twain expressed it best when he stated, "It is easy to quit for I have done it many times before."

If, by chance, you are reading this book, then I succeeded. I succeeded through the many unfinished and incomplete ideas I have had through the last seven years. If not, then I will try again. I am sure of it, "for I have done it many times before."

$$\sim$$

An important truth about this book is understanding that my weaknesses and failures are no different than yours. When I wrote that introduction on the way to Dallas, my resolve was certain. My determination was concrete. But, like many of us, "something" happened in my life, and the most effective coping mechanism I knew of slowly, or I should say rapidly, entered into my daily routine. Once again, I was back to the same place that I had been unsuccessfully trying to escape from for years: smoking pot.

Within the following two years, I finally made it over the hump. I quit smoking for good. In 2006, I thought I was at that point. I could have been at that point. But I chose not to be.

However, I really was dedicated to changing my life. In addition, I was dedicated to actually loving those close to me. I knew that if I was truly going to do that—n action and not just in word— I had to stop. I couldn't allow this habit to control my life. Neither can you.

Which, actually, brings me to the other thing I was dedicated to. I was dedicated to you. I knew, even at that point, that a significant part of my life would be helping others stop this habit that had so robbed me, and them. I knew that they—that you—had obligations, somewhere in your life, which were being ignored. A child. A partner. Another loved one. A career. Yourself. I was dedicated to helping you make your life everything it is intended to be.

I still am.

Several months after I quit smoking, I wrote this:

> We have a tendency to overlook the simple things in life which we are blinded from while living in a cloud of smoke. In fact, it was recognizing these precious little moments that became a major influence for me to continue on with this challenge. Yes, it does remain somewhat of a challenge, even months after the illusion has been removed.
>
> To those who do not yet have children, one of the most amazing experiences you will ever witness is watching a life unfold and discover the multitude of things we have become accustomed to. I will never forget the memory of watching my son discovering his own shadow. As he continued to swipe at his shadow in an apparent attempt to capture it, I could not help reflecting on how many other discoveries I had missed. To not live your life in fulfillment is saddening, but to deny your own child is tragic.
>
> Whether it is an experience with a child or some other circumstance, living a life in captivity to any drug takes more than it gives. I suppose it is somewhat ironic that it took me to discover my own shadow in order to experience my son discovering his.

My goal is to help you experience all the precious moments that life has to offer, and to fully be there for those you love, so you can make many precious moments together. We all want to be able to look back on our lives and say, "I have lived well." I want you to look back some day and say, "I overcame that habit. I loved well. I lived well."

I know, from personal experience, that you can do it.

So . . . where do we begin? You don't climb Mount Everest by throwing on a pair of hiking boots, grabbing a ski cap, and starting to climb. You have to lay a proper foundation. Let's start there.

Rules of Engagement

The fusion of heart and mind in selfless action,
for the betterment of others, to effectively
accomplish the mission and make a difference.

GENERAL REBECCA HALSTEAD,
US Army (Retired), definition of leadership

The most difficult part of writing this book was deciding the order in which the chapters should be placed. Given that there are many of you at different stages in the "quit game," and the diverse challenges you are facing, one chapter somewhere in the middle might be the most important for you.

Some of you have already decided to put an end to the habit, and some of you are still contemplating the idea of quitting. I realize, as well, that at this point some of you don't really intend to stop; rather, you are reading this book because someone is asking (or insisting!) that you do so. Fine. Wherever you are in the process, we can start there.

For those of you who have already quit, read the book as fast as you want and in any order you want. Trust me, you will find helpful information in every section. There might be a chapter toward the end that you should read first. Stay up all night and read the entire book if you want, and then re-read it bit by bit.

For those of you who are starting (or re-starting) to quit, I do recommend this, that you read chapter 20 (and maybe 21) first. Withdrawals will hit, and you will need some concrete ways to help your body through that process. Chapters 20 will give you some great ways to do that. Chapter 21 will, too, in different ways.

Since there are many of you still contemplating or just wanting to get yourselves ready before quitting, you will find this book useful as sort of a manual or guide for making the final decision. Knowing what you are getting yourself into is a very powerful tool. Hopefully, you will also find that the book provides you with encouragement and motivation, while at the same time changing many of the beliefs you have developed surrounding your marijuana use.

And for those of you who are not interested in quitting at this point, the book will still be an interesting read. I believe you will find truth and honesty in the things that are written. All I ask is that you respect the desires of those who are looking to put an end to this habit. If you are a spouse or friend of someone who is making an attempt to quit, please support them. Their decision to stop is a personal one, for whatever reason. Even if you are still smoking, they need your help.

Here are a few suggestions that I believe will be helpful no matter where you are in the game:

- **Read the book first thing in the morning.** If you are reading one chapter per day, this will allow you to begin your day with the motivation or information you need. Recall the chapter throughout the day and what it means to you.

- **Read everything.** Every chapter in the book has a purpose and, hopefully, empowers you in some way.

- **Do not read the book stoned.** This is not a helpful suggestion; *this is a rule*! If you can't follow this simple rule, you shouldn't be reading this book. This is another good reason why those who are still smoking should read the book in the morning.

- **Do not skip the Personal Tasks.** I know for some of you that completing the Personal Tasks may be a little inconvenient. But succeeding at this process requires effort on your part. If you have trouble completing a Personal Task that takes a few minutes out of the day, you might need to rethink your commitment to winning.

Also, before we get started, I want to address several important items.

First: other resources. This book doesn't have to be a stand-alone resource. My website, secretaddiction.org, has an abundance of additional helps, suggestions, and information which can be extremely useful to you achieving your personal goals. From time to time in the book I will refer you to the website for specific resources. In addition, on the website you will find information about my CAARE (Cannabis Addiction And Recovery Empowerment) Program. It is an online, video-based program intended to walk people through the first thirty days of abstinence, and is based upon both the concepts in this book and also my one-on-one work helping people quit.

Second: my position on smoking marijuana. This will become evident through the book, but I want to simply say up front that in this book, I don't take a position on marijuana, as to whether anyone should smoke it, whether it should be legalized, etc. Honestly, that's not what this book is about. This book is about one thing: helping people for whom smoking marijuana is causing ongoing problems in their lives—personally, professionally, relationally, etc. If that is you, this book is for you, and I am dedicated to helping you.

Third: God. I want to say right up front as well that I am a spiritual person, a believer in God. I work with people who believe in God.

I work with people who don't. My goal for both is the same: to help you make your life what you believe it is intended to be and what you want it to be.

Toward the end of the book, I have a chapter about how I think faith in God can fit into the picture of breaking the marijuana habit. If you think that chapter may be helpful to you, great. I do believe that our beliefs and faith can give us hope, strength, and courage. Whatever your personal beliefs are, I encourage you to tap into them for your own hope, strength, and courage.

Whether you believe in God or not, you have to understand that this is ultimately about you. You are responsible to gather the strength to get through this challenge. Didn't you create this problem in the first place? Shouldn't you be the one to take the necessary steps to un-create it?

I will never forget the scene in the movie *Where the Red Fern Grows* when the young boy, Billy, was explaining to his grandfather that he had been praying for God to provide him with the two hunting dogs he wanted. The grandfather's reply is something that I have carried with me since my adolescence. He said, "Son, sometimes you have to meet God halfway."

I have no doubt that God, or the Universe if you wish, will supply the people and things, such as this book you are reading, to assist you in this endeavor. However, it is you who are going to do the work.

So, here's to you. It feels rather odd to be writing this introduction. Although it's at the beginning of the book, it's actually the last thing I've written. It's been a long road. There have been many late nights writing and researching while the rest of the family slept, and many more early mornings before I crept off to work. In regard to your success, I hope that you will put the same dedication and sacrifice into quitting that I have put into writing *The Secret Addiction*. You and I both know that the ideas in this book could change your life forever. They have mine.

PART I

SO YOU WANT TO QUIT

CHAPTER 1

How Did I Get Here?

Sometimes it appears that there is a hidden
Guide whose duty it is to test men through all
sorts of discouraging experiences. Those who pick
themselves up after defeat and keep on trying,
arrive; and the world cries, 'Bravo! I knew you could
do it!' The hidden Guide lets no one enjoy great
achievement without passing the persistence test.
Those who can't take it simply do not make the grade.

NAPOLEON HILL, *Think and Grow Rich*

A natural question for us to ask is: how did I end up in this predicament? It's amazing to me how an addiction sneaks up on people. In fact, often times I wondered, "How in the world did I allow this to happen to me?" I don't have an addictive personality. Or maybe I do. Maybe we all do to a degree. I just chose the wrong thing to become attached to.

Do we get here because we try to convince ourselves repeatedly that there isn't a problem with smoking and that, in some instances, it is actually good for us? Whatever the reason, one thing is certain: given the right circumstances and with enough repetition, it becomes part of our lifestyle. It becomes a part of us, it seems.

Is the real core of the problem the unmanageability of our desires? Not that desire, in and of itself, is a bad thing. It is an essential part of our passion, and drive, to succeed. At some level, though, we failed to distinguish between and pursue the desires that are inherently good or constructive, versus those that are bad or destructive.

But maybe these shouldn't be defined as "bad" or "good" at all. In essence, what we are doing is seeking various ways to comfort ourselves, right? Some just happen to be beneficial and some do not. Most people have areas of their lives that exhibit varying degrees of unmanageability. Right now, the most damaging in your life is your inability to stay away from smoking marijuana. That was certainly the case with my life.

If you could manage your decision or commitment to never smoke again, you would not be reading this book and seeking help in quitting. That is not a negative, however. It is a positive! No man is an island. (Didn't someone say that?) We all need help in getting and staying on a constructive path in life. I certainly did.

The Great Escape

"For me, the underlying force behind my smoking pot comes from the time I actually started to smoke. I'd just emerged from one of life's little crises which had left me battered and bruised. Pot provided a psychological cocoon which I could withdraw into. At the time, this was actually of some benefit to me, but I failed to relinquish this crutch after an appropriate time, and instead continued with impunity." ANONYMOUS

Smoking, for most of us, is an escape . . . an escape from reality. We tend to think that life brings us stress, depression, anxiety, etc. The fact of the matter is that 80% of the things we call stress are self-created.

The other 20% is the reality of life. Friends and family pass away (sometimes tragically), relationships fall apart (sometimes tragically), and some jobs simply end. Whether these stresses are self-created or not, it's how we respond to them that is most important.

What are you running from? What has happened to you (or within you) in the past that has caused you to want to escape reality?

I understand that smoking seems so normal to you, because you have been doing it for so long. How long has it been? Five years? Ten years? How about thirty? I know it must appear to be truly a part of you, but that is a delusion. It's not. When you begin to experience life without pot, you'll see that it was a delusion.

No matter how much you justify your current lifestyle, or no matter how much you trick yourself into believing you are better off clouding your mind with this residue, you are not. You think it empowers you, but like many things we can choose to rely on in life, it renders you less powerful.

The truth is, when the smoke clears, the situation or challenge you are facing is still usually waiting at the door. You will have to face it and deal with it eventually. By not confronting our challenges, they almost always become magnified and create a larger problem. You cannot continue to back yourself into a corner, which ultimately makes you want to escape that much more.

In my opinion, the self-created problems are the worst simply because these are typically a part of who you are as a person. Call it your character, or call it bad habits, but issues such as poor financial responsibility, low self-esteem, or whatever it might be, are underlying problems that need to be addressed. Addressing them is possible, but it takes work! Until you eliminate the regular smoking in your life, the work will never get done.

It is important to understand that the abuse of marijuana is not some character defect that haunts you, but rather a learned behavioral pattern. This learned pattern is usually due to a situation that has occurred repeatedly, such as stress, or even a repeated social activity that leads to a habitual pattern of smoking daily. Of course, you know how the rest of the story goes.

The Real You . . . Exposed

"I started smoking pot as soon as I was out of high school. It was fun. Play some games, watch some TV, and munch out. It was a blast. But it was controlled. I didn't do it constantly. Then the addiction kicked in. It became "a way of life." I'd always be looking forward to getting my work done, so I could get my next fix. Until that reasoning started getting blurred to, "Why don't I get my fix WHILE I'm getting my work done?"

And thus starts the vicious cycle: toke . . . try to work . . . get discouraged . . . convince myself, "Ah, forget it, I'm high, I'll do it later" . . . wait till later and again, "Ah, forget it, I'm burning out, I'll do it tomorrow" . . . wake up the next day feeling ready to work . . . and then, "Well, I'll just take one hit" . . . repeat cycle. When it is all said and done, I manage to meet the deadlines, but just barely. And never to the quality I'm capable of."   ANONYMOUS

Wow! What a great description of a pothead trying to get work done. The description is so true that, when I first read it, I had to laugh. I consider this 20-year-old fortunate that he is waking up to this reality today, and not two decades from now, like many people. At least he is already contemplating quitting. There is no doubt, if he succeeds, it will be a "new life" for him.

What an awesome life . . . living up to his potential. Not a bad idea.

Waking up to who you are is not always a pleasant experience. Often, when we are contemplating the idea of stopping smoking, we think of how remarkable we are going to be when we move from passive to active, disengaged to engaged, not living to living.

Many of the tasks we have been putting off for years will finally get done.

All of the awesome things we are going to do without the weed holding us back is an inspiring thought. Maybe it is starting a new business, spending more time with our kids, reconnecting with friends and family, or some project—like writing a book—that will *finally* get done.

However, the reality is that all of the personal weaknesses we had before we started down the road of marshmallows and video games will still be there. The problem is that many of us have forgotten who we are, and we sometimes create this imaginary superhero that has been held captive by some green monster. For many of us, we have this belief that when we quit smoking, the world around us will magically become perfect.

To the contrary, the world is not perfect, and neither are we. We sometimes neglect to remember our weaknesses such as procrastination, poor self-esteem, fear of rejection, poor management skills, lack of patience, lack of follow-through, negative self-talk, etc. The realization of these problems, when the smoke clears, can be a pretty disappointing experience.

Everyone has personal weaknesses, to a degree, that inherently hold us back in life. In a sense, marijuana allows us to better accept these things about ourselves, but in reality, it simply obscures them, and in the process it creates other problems. The truth is that we need to recognize our problems and start taking steps to overcome them.

Most importantly, you must recognize that you are not going to be the perfect version of yourself for which you had hoped. I am not implying that you need to accept a lesser version of yourself. You now have an opportunity to identify and correct these things for tremendous personal growth. This is often uncomfortable, and takes consistent effort. Even those who seem to have reached the pinnacle of their lives both professionally and personally understand the need of continued improvement.

For some of you, there are issues that you are now going to have to come face to face with. There will be challenges facing those of you who were, or still are, the unfortunate victim of someone else's problems. I wish it were only as easy as understanding that, on some level, people who abuse others, physically and/or verbally, are mostly reacting to the environment in which they were once raised. I know it is much more difficult than to simply "let-go" of the things that have been done. But it has been done before, and therefore can be done again . . . by you.

In the end, it is up to you to take responsibility, and be honest with yourself. At some point, you have to stop blaming others for your circumstances. There might have been people, places, or things that played a key role in your situation, but it is time for you to take ownership. They don't own your life. You do. The more time you continue to blame others for your problems, the less time you spend on taking the necessary action steps to correct them.

Is not life ultimately about challenges? Is not life about looking ahead and knowing that things can improve if only we give 100% in order to achieve a goal? This takes discipline.

Along with discipline, there also has to be a gentleness with self. Shame and self-recrimination do not go very far in helping someone stay sober. It's simply negative thinking, which is what helped get us into this situation in the first place. Why does anyone continue years of daily drug use unless they're highly motivated to escape their own thinking in some way?

When we continue to ignore our personal weaknesses, we find ourselves repeating the same mistakes, which leads to unfulfilled and stressful lives. Do what you have always done, and you will continue to get what you have always gotten. As Einstein said, we can't solve a problem with the same level of thinking that created the problem in the first place. Simply put, nothing will ever change until *you* are ready to make a change!

Just recognizing the necessity of this is a huge step in the right direction. The secret to self-improvement is to admit your fallibilities and begin working to overcome them. Do not let this overwhelm you. The most effective thing you can do is recognize when you are defaulting to your weakness, and then simply do the opposite. It is consistently doing the opposite that counts in the long run. Let me repeat the most important word in that previous sentence . . . consistently.

I know all of you reading this book have a desire for a "better version" of you, or else the thought of quitting would not cross your mind. Mark Twain cleverly noted, "If everyone was satisfied with themselves there would be no heroes." Sure, it will be a little uncomfortable doing the opposite of what your habits are telling you to do, but only at the beginning. The satisfaction and experience of becoming the "new you" will eventually smother the discomfort of change. Besides, "doing what you need to do may not always make you happy, but it will make you great!" I love that quote.

✎ PERSONAL TASK #1
Complete the Marijuana Problem Scale

The Marijuana Problem Scale (MPS) was developed in 1994 by R.S. Stephens and colleagues. It is a self-report assessment that helps you identify areas in your life affected by marijuana use. The MPS contains 19 items that represent potential negative effects of marijuana on social relationships, self-esteem, motivation and productivity, work and finances, physical health, memory impairment, and legal problems.

Once completed, add the number of items reported as a minor problem or serious problem (1 or 2), and compare your score with other individuals from the table following the questionnaire. For Secret Addiction website members, you can also complete the MPS on the Secret Addiction website (secretaddiction.org), which will automatically calculate the comparisons for you.

MARIJUANA PROBLEM SCALE

Following are different types of problems you may have experienced as a result of smoking marijuana. Please circle the number that indicates whether each item has been a problem for you *in the past month*.

HAS MARIJUANA USE CAUSED YOU . . .	NO PROBLEM	MINOR PROBLEM	SERIOUS PROBLEM
1. Problems between you and your partner	0	1	2
2. Problems in your family	0	1	2
3. To neglect your family	0	1	2
4. Problems between you and your friends	0	1	2
5. To miss days at work or miss classes	0	1	2
6. To lose a job	0	1	2

HAS MARIJUANA USE CAUSED YOU . . .	NO PROBLEM	MINOR PROBLEM	SERIOUS PROBLEM
7. To have lower productivity	0	1	2
8. Medical problems	0	1	2
9. Withdrawal symptoms	0	1	2
10. Blackouts or flashbacks	0	1	2
11. Memory loss	0	1	2
12. Difficulty sleeping	0	1	2
13. Financial difficulties	0	1	2
14. Legal problems	0	1	2
15. To have lower energy levels	0	1	2
16. To feel bad about your use	0	1	2
17. Lowered self-esteem	0	1	2
18. To procrastinate	0	1	2
19. To lack self-confidence	0	1	2

MARIJUANA PROBLEM SCALE SCORING INSTRUCTIONS

To obtain the Marijuana Problem Scale (MPS) Score, add the number of items reported as either a *minor problem* or *serious problem*. This score is used in the Marijuana Consequences table on the next page for a comparison to other marijuana users' perceived problems.

MPS Score: _____

MARIJUANA CONSEQUENCES TABLE

MARIJUANA PROBLEM SCORE	ROUNDED PERCENTILE RANKING	MARIJUANA PROBLEM SCORE	ROUNDED PERCENTILE RANKING
0	0	10	57
1	1	11	68
2	3	12	77
3	5	13	85
4	8	14	91
5	11	15	95
6	16	16	98
7	23	17	99
8	32	18	100
9	44	19	100

SOURCES: STEPHENS ET AL. 2000; VENDETTI ET AL. 2002.

This table shows you where you place relative to other adults seeking marijuana treatment. This means that you experience more problems than x (your score) percent of people seeking treatment for their marijuana use.

CHAPTER 2
Why Quit?

I feel as though I have this amazing potential to
be an amazing person but the drug has taken
over that belief and is killing my mental abilities
and confidence. Right now my mind is mush.
I know where I want to go, I know where I want
to be, I know who I want to become, but I can't do
that while my life is revolving around a drug.
ANONYMOUS

You know the saying, "Those who forget their history are doomed to repeat it." Certainly that applies to our personal history with marijuana. Each episode of our history might have different characters, or possibly a different setting, but the story itself never really changes much. To change the story, you have to recall the reason or reasons that smoking has been a bad thing for you. We naturally want to recall the good times and forget everything else that happened. But it's the "everything else that happened" that has landed you where you are right now.

Motivation is often driven by emotion. That's not a bad thing. An emotional desire to change is important. *But it's not sufficient.* Making major life changes almost always requires a stronger foundation than that.

You don't just wake up one day and say to yourself, "You know, I don't want to be a piano teacher anymore. I want to be a chemical engineer." So you watch a few YouTube videos on chemical engineering, and *voila!* you're a chemical engineer.

You're going to have to lay a lot stronger foundation than that. You're going to have to figure out what chemical engineers do, and if that is something you'd be adept at. You're going to make sure you have the time, and the money, to invest in classes. You're going to have to take some prerequisite classes, because those music classes you took aren't going to prepare you for Chem Eng classes. And you're going to need a personal commitment strong enough to make it through 60 or so hours of college credit. Halfway through (or a tenth of the way through!) the going is going to get tough, and life is going to present other challenges, and you'll be tempted to say, "Oh, forget it," and throw in the towel.

Only a solid foundation will see you through all of that.

Someone will say, "But I just kind of slid into being addicted to marijuana. Can't I just kind of slide out of it, too?" Right. Good luck with that. If your willpower is so strong that you can just quit anytime you want to, then here's my challenge: quit for a week. Right now. Starting at the end of this paragraph. Not one toke for the next seven 24-hour periods. After seven full days, come back and start reading again.

~

OK. How did that work out for you? Uh-huh. I thought so.

If you're part of the one percent (or less) who can successfully do that, congratulations! You have almost superhuman ability to alter your habit patterns. Do this three more times (three more weeks) and you are well on your way to a smoke-free life.

For the rest of us mere mortals, as I said before, we need a much more solid foundation for change than that. That's what this chapter is about.

I will admit that it is difficult to maintain the same amount of enthusiasm for something from day to day, year after year. So there has to be a fundamental change in you that takes place, and not just emotionally. However, any motivation you have now is helpful in preparing you and catapulting you through the first few weeks of this process, while you build a solid foundation.

I am certain that many of you already have your reasons for quitting. Unless, of course, you are being pressured to read this book. In that case, you may simply be turning the pages and pretending to be reading by nodding your head as if you are in agreement. If you don't relate right now to what's in this book, fine. I'm guessing that one day you will, so in the meantime hold onto it.

The point I am trying to make is that your underlying motivation is the gas that fuels your car, so to speak. It is such an important ingredient to your success, and it is imperative it not be forgotten. Most of you will have a day (days, actually) when your mind attempts to play tricks on you, and tells you that just one smoke won't hurt anything, that you can go right back to your abstinence without any problem. On those days, it's so easy to forget your reasons for quitting in the first place, or somehow convince yourself that those reasons aren't so important after all.

Nonsense. Whatever your specific reasons for quitting, they are *very* important. Otherwise, you never would have thought about quitting in the first place, much less made and followed through with the commitment to actually do it. No one quits pot because they think, "You know, this isn't causing me much of a problem, but it might make my life just slightly better if I stopped." People stop because they come to the place where they think, "This is causing some real problems for me and for those I care about, and for my own sake and for theirs, I really need to stop."

It's that rationale that you need to keep at the forefront of your mind. That's why laying the foundation is so important.

I will never forget the day I learned my wife was pregnant with our first child. For some reason, I thanked God that this new discovery was my ticket to finally escaping this horrible habit. Having a child made it so different, I thought. But, once again, I conveniently placed that event into my pile of unsuccessful motivations as soon as the opportunity presented itself.

Our faulty reasoning during times of weakness can be so powerful that we often forget why we made the decision to quit. *Never* forget why you want to be away from this stranglehold of isolation, stagnation, and lack of motivation.

The Personal Task at the end of this chapter will assist you in identifying your own reasons for quitting. It is also an opportunity to list your personal goals for your life. It's important that you complete it when you've finished this chapter. Before you take that step, however, let's spend a few minutes looking at some of the major reasons people have for wanting to quit in the first place.

Financial Costs

You need to take a good look at the financial costs of drug use, because it can be a real eye-opener, especially to those of us who smoked more than just a few years. It's not just the cost of the pot. When you factor in all of the other things that chronic marijuana smoking costs you, it is pretty sad. For any financial cost calculation, you have to add in the cost of papers, pipes, bongs, and any other paraphernalia you have purchased. What about all the extra food you eat? Five extra dollars a day for the munchies? That's over $1800 a year. Oh, and let's not forget the greatest expense of all: time and opportunity.

It's not that easy to calculate time and opportunity, but just imagine the magnitude. Take a moment and think about what else or who else could have used or needed the money you wasted on this drug? Or who could have benefitted from what you could have accomplished from the opportunity that all of that time presented.

This exercise isn't meant to beat up on ourselves. It's meant to get us honest with ourselves. "Hey, this habit has cost me a hell of a lot, and I just laid it all out!" Sometimes facing the truth isn't the most pleasant thing, but it's essential to do if we are going to be serious about making positive changes in our lives.

Complete the Financial Cost Calculator now. (A more comprehensive financial cost calculator is available for members on the website, secretaddiction.org.)

✎ PERSONAL TASK #2
Financial Cost Calculator

How much do you estimate you spend weekly
   on the following items:

Marijuana $_____

Marijuana Paraphernalia $_____

Extra Food associated with your habit $_____

Opportunity Cost of the time you spend smoking $_____

Sum: Total Weekly Cost $_____

                                                              x 52

Total Annual Cost: $_____

Lost Opportunity

*"I can't tell you how many times I have lied to my parents
or other important figures in my life just to keep my secret.
But I'm tired of hiding from everyone, and I'm tired of wasting
my days and my money. I only bought the good stuff, which
I calculated was costing me $3,000 a year, not including food,
pipes, and of course the lost opportunity cost."*   ANONYMOUS

The individual who wrote the quote above was very perceptive at realizing the cost of "lost opportunity." I am sure this outweighs the monetary expenses of smoking the stuff by a wide margin. There are many who appear to be smoking and succeeding in life, but there can be a thin line between mediocrity and greatness. Have a .300 batting average as a major league baseball player and you're probably a hall of famer. Have a .250 batting average and you may well not even be a starting player. What's the difference? One extra hit every twenty at bats.

There is no denying that kicking the habit is a challenge. For many of you it may end up being the greatest challenge of your life. But the fact is, we all have challenges, many of which we create. Every challenge is nothing more than a chance to achieve something better. To avoid them is to avoid growth and progress. To repeat them crushes our self-esteem.

Obviously, we have to identify the challenge first. Becoming self-aware concerning your "secret" is one the greatest opportunities you will ever have. In his book, *The Greatness Guide*, Robin Sharma wrote:

Our awareness precedes choice and our choice precedes
results. With better awareness of what needs to improve
in your life, you can make better choices. And with better
choices, you will see better results.

You have to keep your awareness on the destination you have chosen. Otherwise, you might choose to take a wrong turn and, as in many cases, head down the wrong path again before you are able to get to the other side of this mountain. There is no doubt that the beginning of this journey is a bumpy road uphill, but it is does smooth out the further you travel.

I hope there are people who will support you through this climb, but you are the one who is in control. You make the decisions. This book is only one tool for you to utilize. Do not just sit and wait for things to unfold. You have to actively participate in the process. Listen to the suggestions and follow the advice of those who have been here before you. The people who have succeeded have also failed many times. What they have to say is invaluable. I look forward to seeing you on the other side of this mountain.

How Low Can You Go?

"I feel like a bit of a loser right now. I just went rummaging through the freaking garbage looking for my pipe to try and smoke some resin. I couldn't find it, though. What a sorry sight! It is 15° and snowing outside, and I went through that crap four times looking for it. I emptied it out on the yard, and used a freaking rake for crying out loud. I guess I will take this as a sign."   ANONYMOUS

If we think about it, we will have to admit to ourselves that we've probably done some pretty humiliating things to satisfy our urge to smoke. Granted, these things may not be the same as some of the horrific stories we hear about crack/cocaine addicts, and the lengths they will go just to score their drug. In fact, some of the stories about marijuana users may even be a little comical. But, if we take a moment to really evaluate our actions, these stories are embarrassing, and in some cases, utterly shameful. When I first read the confession above, the realization about my own past actions really set in.

As I said, looking back at those times, in a way, is a little humorous now, but just a little. There was a time when it frustrated and embarrassed me that I had become what I knew I really wasn't meant to be. Our actions and behaviors change dramatically when we are held captive by the desire to obtain something that has so much control over us. We constantly sacrifice our sense of right and wrong. We make excuses for ourselves, so our self-worth is not offended. But in the end, we aren't really fooling ourselves. We have hugely lowered our standards of what we should be so that we can satisfy the need. And we know it.

If you are just beginning this journey toward wholeness, many of these memories are still very fresh. The many reasons you have decided to quit once-and-for-all hinge on some of these past actions. Don't forget about those moments! As humans, we have this unique ability to only remember the "good times" when we begin to miss our "little companion."

That's just human nature. We do this when we break up with boyfriends and girlfriends too. Somehow our brains fall into a cloud of romantic amnesia, and we invite them back into our lives. But that never works out in the end, does it? OK, there are a few exceptions in relationships. A few people do actually get back with old boyfriends/girlfriends and it works out long-term.

You know what? It *never* works out that way with pot. I've never talked to someone who got to the point of breaking up with pot, who then got back into that pot relationship and said to me years later, "This has worked out great! I don't know why I ever wanted to break up in the first place!"

If you can direct me to anyone like that, they'll be the first I've ever met.

So, think about it. What have you done in the past to obtain marijuana that you would not have done otherwise? Who have you ignored in your life so that you could stay at home, and remain isolated in your smoking refuge? How low have you gotten to look for scattered remnants of marijuana?

For me, the most regretted remembrance of those days were the selfish acts that I committed. The fact that I neglected my wife and child was and still is, to some degree, heartbreaking. The way my oldest child looks at me now is different, because I am different. I was never a bad father, but I was never a truly committed father. My second child, thankfully, doesn't know the old me. All he sees is the father I am supposed to be.

All of the bad memories finally pass. Everything (well, most everything) does become an indistinct memory as you begin to live your life differently. People you have shunned enter back into your life, and those you have connected with, simply because of marijuana, gradually fade away. As we stop crawling on the floor looking for scraps and instead stand upright, our purpose and our perception of the world we live in changes.

Food for Thought

> *"Marijuana is a sneaky little devil. It tricks you into thinking that there is no way it is going to be a problem and then, before you know it, a decade or two of your life is gone and you can barely remember any of it."* ANONYMOUS

Why do we deceive ourselves? Is there anything in your life that is as complete or fulfilled as it would be if you were not smoking? Really, this is about maximizing your potential.

What about your relationships? Many of us avoid even the most precious relationships in our lives. Is there a spouse you have neglected? Are you truly the father or mother you thought you would be? Have you neglected family members, significant others, friends, and co-workers? Equally important, have you neglected yourself?

Aren't the trials associated with quitting marijuana worth the reward of having fulfilling relationships, such as with your children? What if your children grow up to follow in your footsteps with this habit?

Stop and think for a moment about where you are in life compared to where you thought you would be. Think of the people who have been affected by your addiction. How many people have drifted away from you? How many have come into your life who really shouldn't be there?

What about your health? Is that a concern to you? Are you overeating, primarily with all the wrong foods? What about your activity level? Is it video games and TV? Apart from overeating and possible lack of physical activity, how in the world can you focus on what is beneficial for your health and ignore the fact that you are engulfing your lungs with copious amounts of smoke?

What about your mental acuity? Have you noticed that you are less able to find exact words to express yourself? What about other people having difficulty understanding what you mean? Do you have problems in understanding what other people mean? Do you have feelings of being misunderstood?

Do you experience feelings of loneliness? Do you feel often feel inadequate and unsuccessful? Have you noticed that you often repeat your mistakes?

Is this what you envisioned that you wanted for your life? If not, why are you still heading down this path? By now I think everyone has heard this colloquial definition: insanity is doing the same thing over and over and expecting a different result. Not to clinically question anyone's mental fitness, but is the path you're on insane?

The following is a list of just a few of the common motivations people have for quitting, listed in the *Brief Counseling for Marijuana Dependence* manual:

- Put off actions and decisions to the point of being a burden on family and friends
- Given up personal aspirations
- Had nagging health concerns, such as worries about lung damage
- Made excuses for unfinished tasks or broken promises
- Experienced disapproval from family and friends
- Been involved in the criminal justice system

I realize that all of these questions I have raised, and all of these issues, may not apply to you. Your life may have had enough serious consequences from smoking that the answers are pretty obvious. Maybe they aren't. If not, congratulations! You can choose to turn this around before you do experience them. Either way, a better life awaits you. Why would you possibly want to say no to it?

Positive Goals

So far, we have only mentioned the negative motivators, such as the conditions or situations we would like to avoid. These are powerful, but what about those that are positive? What are some goals you would like to achieve, once you have given up smoking? Ask any person who is successful what motivates him/her, and very likely the answer will be "goals." Goal setting is extremely important to motivation and success.

So what goals have been put on hold for the last five, ten, or twenty years? As George Eliot said, "It's never too late to be who you might have been." What are your motivations? Personal Task #3 will help you think this through.

✐ PERSONAL TASK #3
Reasons for Quitting Questionnaire

Personal Task #3 will assist you in identifying your reasons to quit. The Reasons for Quitting Questionnaire is based on earlier work with tobacco cessation and has been modified based on initial results with people who use marijuana and seek treatment.

The 26 items assess reasons for quitting marijuana in the following broad categories: health concerns, desire for self-control, and social and legal influences. It is an excellent tool to help you stay on track by recalling why you decided to stop smoking in the first place. We have a tendency to replace the reasons *not to smoke* with reasons *to smoke* when the going gets a little tough.

Personal Task #3 also provides an opportunity to list your goals. This includes any personal, professional, or even play goals. This will empower you and strengthen your desire to put an end to this cycle. As I mentioned, we all have a tendency to forget the "whys." Therefore, as you read through the book, return to your answers to the Reasons for Quitting Questionnaire and review them often.

People who want to stop smoking marijuana may have several reasons for quitting. I am interested in finding out your reasons for wanting to quit. There are no right or wrong reasons. Any reason is a good one. Below is a list of reasons that a person may have. Please read each statement and circle the number that best describes how much this reason applies to you at this time.

I WANT TO QUIT SMOKING MARIJUANA AT THIS TIME	NOT AT ALL	A LITTLE BIT	MOD-ERATELY	QUITE A BIT	VERY MUCH
1. To show myself that I can quit if I want to	0	1	2	3	4
2. Because I will like myself better if I quit	0	1	2	3	4

I WANT TO QUIT SMOKING MARIJUANA AT THIS TIME	NOT AT ALL	A LITTLE BIT	MOD-ERATELY	QUITE A BIT	VERY MUCH
3. Because I won't have to leave social functions or other people's houses to smoke	0	1	2	3	4
4. So that I can feel in control of my life	0	1	2	3	4
5. Because my family and friends will stop nagging me if I quit	0	1	2	3	4
6. To get praise from people I'm close to	0	1	2	3	4
7. Because smoking marijuana does not fit in with my self-image	0	1	2	3	4
8. Because smoking marijuana is becoming less socially acceptable	0	1	2	3	4
9. Because someone has told me to quit or else	0	1	2	3	4
10. Because I will receive a special gift if I quit	0	1	2	3	4
11. Because of potential health problems	0	1	2	3	4
12. Because people I am close to will be upset if I don't quit	0	1	2	3	4
13. So that I can get more things done	0	1	2	3	4
14. Because I have noticed that smoking marijuana is hurting my health	0	1	2	3	4
15. Because I want to save the money I spend on marijuana	0	1	2	3	4
16. To prove that I am not addicted to marijuana	0	1	2	3	4
17. Because there is a drug testing policy at work	0	1	2	3	4
18. Because I know others with health problems caused by smoking marijuana	0	1	2	3	4
19. Because I am concerned that smoking marijuana will shorten my life	0	1	2	3	4

I WANT TO QUIT SMOKING MARIJUANA AT THIS TIME	NOT AT ALL	A LITTLE BIT	MOD-ERATELY	QUITE A BIT	VERY MUCH
20. Because of legal problems related to marijuana	0	1	2	3	4
21. Because I don't want to be a bad example for children	0	1	2	3	4
22. Because I want to have more energy	0	1	2	3	4
23. So that my hair and clothes won't smell like marijuana	0	1	2	3	4
24. So that I won't burn holes in clothes or furniture	0	1	2	3	4
25. Because my memory will improve	0	1	2	3	4
26. So that I will be able to think more clearly	0	1	2	3	4

SOURCE: BRIEF COUNSELING FOR MARIJUANA DEPENDENCE MANUAL

Use the spaces below to list your three most important reasons for wanting to stop smoking marijuana. If any of the statements above are among your most important reasons, list them in the spaces below. Otherwise, write your own reasons.

My three most important reasons, in order of importance, for wanting to quit smoking marijuana are:

1. _____
2. _____
3. _____

REASONS FOR QUITTING QUESTIONNAIRE SCORING INSTRUCTIONS

For a total *Reasons for Quitting (RFQ) Score*, add the number of items reported as a reason to quit smoking marijuana. Count only those responses coded as 2, 3, or 4 (*moderately, quite a bit, or very much*).

Include any open-ended items in the list of 3 above that are not on the list of 26 in the table.

RFQ Score: _____

If you have not yet quit smoking marijuana, circle the number that indicates how ready you are RIGHT NOW to stop smoking marijuana.

0%---------20%---------40%---------60%---------80%---------100%

Not ready to quit   **Ready to quit**

If you have stopped smoking marijuana already, circle the number that indicates how ready you are RIGHT NOW to remain abstinent.

0%---------20%---------40%---------60%---------80%---------100%

**Not ready to   Ready to quit/
remain abstinent   remain absinent**

CHAPTER 3

Parent to Parent

As much as we watch to see what our children do with their lives, they are watching us to see what we do with ours. I can't tell my children to reach for the sun. All I can do is reach for it, myself.

Joyce Maynard

To those of you who have children, what I am about to write is really out of concern for your kids, and your relationship with them. Why? Well, in the words of Robert Fulghum, "Don't worry that children never listen to you; worry that they are always watching you."

This chapter could easily have been placed at the end of Chapter 2, for it is another answer to the "why quit?" question. But I have separated it out into its own separate chapter to emphasize its importance. It is *very* important.

If you have children, or may soon have children, this chapter is specifically for you. If you do not, it is still worth reading, because it is likely that someday your lifestyle will deeply influence children—your own kids, your nieces and nephews, etc.

First, let's discuss the younger ones who don't have a clue that mommy or daddy smokes. Many of our children are so young that they are not aware of the habit. In some cases, we may feel they have not suffered because of it. Obviously, we keep this dirty little secret from them for a reason. However, as they get older, if you continue the "habit," they will eventually discover your secret, and then you have to respond.

One response is to quit. However, quite honestly, this is not likely if you have not already stopped on your own accord.

The other response is to somehow justify your use or admit to your addiction. Believe it or not, there are some that, instead of giving up the habit, would rather have everyone around them smoking, including their children. Sad but true. This may allow an individual to feel better about their dependence, but it is the most selfish approach I can imagine. Even most of these parents would advise their children not to start down the same road.

How do you think children are going to react to this? Probably in one of two ways. The first, God forbid, is to take up the habit and simply use the same justifications that you yourself use. What if, as is common, they end up being users whom weed dumbs down and makes far less functional? You then will have initiated a life of clouded, unfulfilled aspirations for the very people you care about the most.

Why would any parent hand a loaded gun to a child and have them risk their lives and future? Haven't you played with this loaded gun long enough and been on the losing end? What are the possibilities of your child following in your footsteps? Anyone who has been around children long enough has seen how they mimic anything the parent does. They are, in many cases, carbon copies of their parents.

Marijuana is already prevalent and readily available to your children. Estimates indicate that 16%, 32%, and 37% of 8th, 10th, and 12th graders, respectively, have used pot in the previous year. Among 12th graders who used, approximately 20% report using it daily. More importantly, youth aged twenty and under comprise over half of all treatment admissions for marijuana abuse in the U.S., and marijuana is reported to be the primary drug of abuse in the majority of all adolescent substance abuse admissions (SAMHSA, 2001).

Based on these statistics, there is a good chance your child will be exposed to the drug outside of the home. On what basis are you going to tell him or her to not use it? Since they know you use it, which is going to speak louder to them, your words or your actions? Your words, maybe? Are you kidding?

It's much likelier that your actions (and, eventually, your own words) will teach them your own rationalizations and justifications, and thereby encourage them to smoke like you do. After all, if these rationalizations are good enough for mom or dad, why aren't they good enough for them?

What if, on the other hand, your child has developed a "no drug" attitude and then discovers that his mother or father are drug addicts? At this point, you may lose the respect of the very ones you hold so dear. This actually haunted me more than trying to justify my use. I know I shouldn't have to say this, but being a parent carries a huge responsibility. To teach your kids about your experiences, and to help encourage and guide them through life, is a massive undertaking.

As a father to two boys, I truly want them to gain the advantages of having a father in their lives they can respect. Too many of our children these days are missing the parental influences so necessary for their growth and development. Simply put, I want to be a role model to my children.

I know I am not perfect. What parent is? And I know that, regardless of my imperfections, my kids will love me, overlook my many flaws, and see the father I aspire to be. But for my kids to know that I handle life through smoking a plant isn't the role model they should be looking up to. No matter how much we may justify using, drug dependency demonstrates weakness, not strength. It doesn't engender respect. It just doesn't.

Some of you reading this book have already allowed your children to start down this road. Since you are taking the steps toward abstinence, you have obviously come to the realization that marijuana is addictive. I can only imagine how you must feel, knowing that you somehow played a role in permitting your child to begin the same journey.

It's important not to be too hard on yourself. That doesn't help anyone, especially your children.

When you are involved with a drug that captivates so much of your life, it's not uncommon to have those close to you enter into the same prison. Your thinking at the time was probably so flawed that you may have truly believed, at some level, that your smoking seemed OK. You could only see the good in smoking. That's the nature of drug addiction.

Whatever was the case, that's water under the bridge. We have to live in the here and now. You are a role model for your children at any age, no matter what has transpired in the past. Your children want to believe in you and to respect you, but they have to trust you first. As I have said, anything that you have created in your life, you have the ability to UN-create. I can't tell you how much your children seeing you go through the process of quitting and sticking with it will mean for their lives. It will be huge for them.

CHAPTER 4

Why Do People Fail?

One of the most common causes of failure is
the habit of quitting when one is overtaken
by temporary defeat. Every person is guilty
of this mistake at one time or another.

Napoleon Hill, *Think and Grow Rich*

R ight up front, I want to talk about why people fail in their
attempts to quit marijuana. Giving up an addiction that has had
a grip on you, or has become a "part of you," is not easy. In fact, failure is so common it seems to be part of the process. It's vital that you
come to an understanding of failure and have a plan to deal with it.

In this chapter we will look at the common reasons that people
fail in their attempts to quit. We will also look at several realities
that, upon first glance, may seem contradictory:

- Failure can make you weak
- Failure can be a vital part of the quitting process
- Smoking "occasionally" as a quitting strategy doesn't work

I told you these might seem contradictory. They aren't, but
they do exist in a certain tension. That will make more sense as
we explore why.

But first, let's look at why people experience failure.

If you've read over 30 pages into this book, you are probably thinking seriously about quitting yourself. Either that, or someone *wants* you to think seriously about it. Maybe you went through Chapter 1 and admitted for the first time, "You know, marijuana seems to be causing some real problems in my life; maybe I need to consider quitting." Maybe you were already at that point, and Chapter 1 simply affirmed what you already knew. Maybe you picked up this book having already made a definite internal commitment to quit. Maybe you've already tried quitting numerous times, and you picked up this book hoping to find a resource that will help you succeed.

Most of us start out the process of quitting by thinking that it's not going to be that difficult. After all, we simply made certain choices to get us to where we are now. We can just make certain choices to, essentially, retrace our steps, can't we?

If only it were that simple.

I used to be envious of those individuals we have heard about who, for whatever reason, made a sudden decision to quit and then succeeded. After years of daily smoking—or whatever addiction that had held them captive—they made quitting look easy. Now, I realize there was probably more to these stories than I knew. Many people we know of who have quit suddenly have also had an under-lying emotional event or reason prompting the decision to stop. That often-dramatic event or reason produced unusual strength in the decision to quit. The critical factor is not the event; plenty of people have failed to translate dramatic events into actually quit-ting. Rather, *the critical factor is the strength of the decision to quit.*

For those people who continue to talk about how they can quit anytime they want, either they have never made the attempt, or they are just lying to themselves. In fact, I'll repeat the challenge to any one of you who might be reading this book out of simple curi-osity, or maybe you were prompted to do so by someone you know:

STOP SMOKING FOR ONE WEEK!

That's right. I want you to stop smoking for one week. Anyone can stop for two or three days, but there is something special about the one-week mark that makes it a little more difficult. You can always go back to smoking after the week, so that should make it a little easier. But there are a few rules you have to follow:

- Not one toke or you have failed, and this proves my point.
- You can't do this while out of town on vacation or for work. You have to do this in your normal environment.
- This means seven full days and not just during the work week. In fact, if you want a real challenge, then start on a Saturday.

The majority of you who are willing to take on this challenge will find that it is more difficult than you think. Now, imagine what lies ahead for those who have dedicated themselves to life-long abstinence. At least with a temporary situation like this, it is a little more comforting knowing that after one week you can resume smoking again.

Regardless of whether you have already tried to quit or not, it's important to understand the primary reasons people fail. Some of you will need to make sure everything in the list is addressed. However, a few, and I mean very few, will not need to address any of these simply because the reason or decision not to smoke is powerful enough to carry you through. DO NOT count on yourself as being one of the few.

Here, I have found, are the most common reasons people fail:

- **A weak commitment** – To succeed at anything takes commitment. If you approach this challenge without a strong commitment to see yourself though the difficult periods, then . . . well, you have failed.

- **A negative attitude** – Perhaps Dr. Larry Markson said it best in *Talking to Yourself is Not Crazy*:

  I want you to stop thinking and talking negatively; it cannot help you in any way. And while you are at it, stop putting yourself down, stop complaining at any cost, stop associating with anyone who does not make you feel better about yourself, stop giving others permission to keep you from being great, stop being timid, stop whining and instead go the other way.

- **An unwillingness to change** – If you are not willing to make changes in your life, habits, or surroundings, you will most definitely remain stuck in your situation. This is the #1 reason that people continue to get the same results out of life, whether good or bad.

- **A short-cut mindset** – Not to be negative, but the road to success is really never the easiest road to take. There are twists, curves and bumps along the way. Wanting to take a short cut means never learning about the cliff waiting for you around the corner—a cliff that, more than likely, you will go over!

- **Lack of information** – Information is empowering; information is empowering. That wasn't a typo . . . it's just that important to repeat it. Information is empowering.

- **Lack of support** – I really can't think of any successful person who has not had the support of someone else. The more committed support systems you have through this process, the better chances you have at succeeding. More on this later.

- **No plan or goals** – Unless you have had some epiphany that rocked you to the core and provoked this decision, you will need to have a plan to achieve your ultimate goal of abstinence. This book will help you develop a plan and eventually allow you to achieve this goal.

- **No long-term vision** – This is not about short-term success. This is a lifetime decision that requires you to be able to clearly see yourself and your life in the future without the daily habit of smoking.

As I will say many times, all of this starts with a choice. You need to get back into the driver's seat. This is one of the most important decisions you will ever make. Preceding this decision is the desire to quit. The desire to be a better person, perform better at home or work, or to be healthier is the seed that will continually allow you to pick yourself up after a failure and carry on with your decision.

Failure Can Be a Negative . . . Or a Positive

Chances are good that if you commit to quitting, and stop smoking, you will encounter some failure. Most people do. But that doesn't mean we accommodate it, or use it as an excuse. We never *plan* to fail. What we do is *make plans to keep going* if we do temporarily fail.

The biggest problem with repeated failure is that it wears us down. After many failed attempts, you may begin to view yourself as weak, and your confidence and the certainty needed to overcome this problem is lost.

Do not allow this to happen. True, setbacks are a part of the process for most. But it is not until we fail (for some of us many, many times) that we realize we have lost control. It is usually not until after many failures that we begin to take the situation seriously.

I had reached a point after attempting to quit and failing so often—as soon as I hit a crisis, a party, a good meal, or whatever I used as my excuse at the time—that I began to seriously question my own strength. For the first time, I began to realize that I was no longer in the driver's seat concerning this situation. This is an intimidating realization.

The truth is that whether failure wears us down and causes us to lose hope, or whether it brings us to a greater realization as to the seriousness of our situation and strengthens our resolve to take the necessary steps to overcome it, is really up to us. We are in control of how we choose to respond. There are many times we fail in life, but we only lose if we give up. Thankfully, many of us have chosen not to give up even after many failures, including myself.

I would not have been able to write this book without the experience that comes from the failures I have encountered throughout the years. It may seem strange, but I cherish each and every one of those failures, no matter how difficult they might have seemed at the time. Ultimately, I chose to respond to my failures in a positive way, and used them to lead me (and others) to a much better place. You can do the same.

Occasionally Does Not Work

As we discuss failure, one common misconception needs to be dispensed with right up front. It's the idea that you can stop smoking marijuana by simply deciding to smoke occasionally. It just doesn't work.

One marijuana user reported the following in his journal:

"Well, I posted last Sunday that I was going to quit the next day . . . but I didn't. I feel bad to have failed, especially because I really thought I was ready this time and mentally strong enough to do it. However, all is not lost because before when

I've tried and failed to give up, I've just gone straight back to smoking as much as before. Also, I have always had to have a stash of weed, but this week I haven't phoned my dealer at all— the weed I've smoked has been with friends. I haven't had that security blanket of knowing I have a smoke at home. I have just not resisted temptation when it's presented itself! This is not what I wanted, but I guess it is progress of sorts!" ANONYMOUS

Not really. Maybe it is a different path to failure, but I wouldn't call it progress. If I were to look into my crystal ball at the time of this post, a call to his dealer was only a couple of days away. It's my experience that this "every once in a while" program does not work 99.9% of the time. If you continue to allow this "ex" of yours to come over and spend time with you, she will move back in.

What most of us will do to help soften the blow of quitting is to allow the occasional smoke on the weekends, or after a certain time in the evenings. During my many attempts to quit, I, too, tried to "ration" my use by confining it only to weekends. This is a breeding ground for failure. Once an abuser, always an abuser.

Communicating with others, either to help or be helped, is very important to the quitting process. Over the years I've noticed a common trend of many people who, in an online post, are contemplating, or justifying, the idea of becoming only an occasional smoker. The problem is that we never hear from them again. Obviously, this approach does not work.

One of the most common reasons people give for "accidentally" smoking again is that they are hanging with friends. You're having a good time, maybe drinking a little, and then . . . BOOM! . . . you're driving home kicking yourself, because after all of the torture to stop, you trip up at a party and your mouth lands right on top of the bong. You have to be on constant alert for that "one moment."

Many people reward themselves with the occasional smoke, like a prisoner gets a few hours in the yard for good behavior. If you truly want to be free, then some of the things you have to do will not be easy. It takes work, not just mind control. I am not only speaking from personal experience, but also from the accounts of many others who seem to disappear into the night never to be heard from again. Well, at least until the next attempt to quit.

Just Get Rid of It

If you are not ready mentally, or do not have a plan in place for quitting, then continue to smoke while you are preparing yourself for your stop date. However, if you think you are ready to quit, but for some reason you are keeping weed or your paraphernalia in the house, you are wasting your time. You're not yet serious about quitting.

In fact, as you read through the book, there will be various "rules of engagement" that I feel are important to your success. Holding onto your paraphernalia or a small amount of marijuana, "just in case," will be the first of those, and certainly the most important to your success or failure.

Having easy access to weed when your "other self" has convinced you, or given you a reason to smoke, is making it too easy for you to fail. You may have heard the story of the general who, when landing on shore for battle, instructed his men to burn their ships so that there was no way of retreat. His men had no choice but to fight for their lives, or die. They won. If you follow this rule, you can too.

Simply cutting back or reducing the times you smoke very rarely works. If you think you can smoke "every now and again," then go for it. But why waste the time trying something that will almost certainly bring you right back to where you were in the first place? "Buck up" and get clean. You can do it, if you work it.

How come we never see a crack or heroin addict try to ration their use when quitting? It's a strategy we often hear about in marijuana circles. No matter what drug you are using, you are still someone who has lost control of your use patterns. Allowing it to somehow stay in your life will eventually permit it to move right back into the forefront.

The main point of this section is to convince you to throw away any paraphernalia you have held onto and to throw away any weed you might have stashed in the sock drawer, even if you are keeping it there to show how much control you think you have over it.

For those of you who have decided to go this alone, while your partner or roommate continues to smoke, you need to create guidelines for their use when around you. If these people are not ready to make the change with you, then they should be considerate or respectful enough to conceal it from your view. When the temptation comes, or the daily reminder of the smell and experiences, it is too easy to succumb knowing there is a stash only a few feet away.

This is one of the most difficult situations to deal with when someone is attempting to quit. Having a partner who is willing to participate in your failure, by having you continue to smoke, is a very selfish act. If this is the case, serious thought and consideration into removing this individual from your life should be given. The wrong kind of "friends" can have a very detrimental influence.

I know the feeling of being in a situation where you wonder if "one more time" would be worth it. From experience, I can tell you that it isn't.

To finish the chapter the same way we began, I will use a quote from one of the best books ever written about success, *Think and Grow Rich* by Napoleon Hill:

> A burning desire to be and to do is the starting point from which the dreamer must take off. Dreams are not born of indifference, laziness, or lack of ambition. Remember that all who succeed in life get off to a bad start, and pass through many heartbreaking struggles before they arrive.

CHAPTER 5

What It Takes to Quit

If you listen to some people, you'd think that most addictions are a life sentence of destruction and despair. Addictions are almost impossible to overcome. It takes superhuman effort that most of us just don't have.

All of that is false. People quit addictions all the time. In fact, most people end up quitting most addictions. They get to the point that their desire to quit has grown larger than their desire to continue, and they are willing to endure some temporary unpleasantness to make positive change in their lives.

In his ground-breaking book *The Surprising Truth about Addiction,* Stanton Peele offers an explanation that helps eliminate the self-defeating thoughts we have about our lack of self-control. There is hope in his message to many of you who are at the point of giving up on trying to quit or are unable to visualize an end to this era in your life.

> More people quit addictions than maintain them, and they do so on their own. That's not to say it happens overnight. People succeed when they recognize that the addiction interferes with something they value—and when they develop the confidence that they can change.
>
> Change is natural. You no doubt act very differently in many areas of your life now compared with how you did when you were a teenager. Likewise, over time you will

probably overcome or ameliorate certain behaviors: a short temper, crippling insecurity.

Kicking these habits constitutes a dramatic change, but the change need not occur in a dramatic way. Successful treatment places the responsibility for change squarely on the individual and acknowledges that positive events in other realms may jump-start change.

Consider the experience of American soldiers returning from the war in Vietnam, where heroin use and addiction was widespread. In 90 percent of cases, when GIs left the pressure cooker of the battle zone, they also shed their addictions—*in vivo* proof that drug addiction can be just a matter of where in life you are.

Most addicts of any sort *do* stop. So the chances are good that at some point in your life you *will* stop smoking marijuana.

So, is that an excuse just to put off stopping for another week, or month, or year, or ten years?

No! Just the opposite. Understanding this reality should be the ultimate incentive to stop now, *before* the addiction brings more damage to you, your relationships, your career, or the ones you love. Your thought process should be this:

- I *will* overcome this addiction at some point in my life.
- Therefore, I am *able* to overcome this addiction. Telling myself otherwise is a lie.
- By far the wisest choice I can make for myself and for those close to me is to take whatever steps are necessary to overcome it *now*. I simply don't have an excuse not to.

So what does it actually take to overcome an addiction? It takes three things:

- Being willing to face reality

- Changing your beliefs
- Changing your habits

That's it. That's what it takes.

Of course, if you're like me, you focus on that last one and say to yourself, "Yeah, right. If I could just snap my fingers and change my habits, I would have by now!"

The vital thing to realize is that all of three of these work in tandem. Confronting the reality of where you are in life right now (which is what we've been doing in this first part of the book so far) enables you to start changing your beliefs. And changing your beliefs is critical—and I do mean critical—to being able to change your habits.

In reality, smoking is not the problem. You have no problem smoking. Stopping is not the problem, either. Most of you have a variety of ways to stop smoking. *Staying stopped* is the problem. If you had the willpower to stop starting again, you would have no problem with marijuana.

So, is the dilemma a lack of willpower? Fighting this with willpower alone will make for a very difficult fight. No one is suggesting that you simply need to exert more willpower and that will get you over the hump. You will need to make choices, yes, but you will have many more resources to rely upon than simple willpower.

Ultimately, the critical ingredient in permanent change is eliminating your desire for pot. If you don't want to smoke pot, you won't. It's as simple as that. I don't want to smoke pot anymore, so I don't.

I'll use long-distance running as an example. Some people do long-distance running so much that it starts to harm their health. This may not be a problem for most runners, but for some it is. Their bodies can no longer take the pounding. Nevertheless, they keep running, *even though it is hurting them,* because they *want* to run. They are addicted to it.

Chances are, this isn't a problem for you. Why? Because you don't *want* to run ten miles a day. That's just not a major temptation in your life. You're not having to resist with all your might the urge to go out and run ten miles, because you just don't want to.

Smoking marijuana is no different. You will get to the place where you just don't want to do it anymore. I'm not saying that you won't have times when you think to yourself, "You know, it was kind of fun, being high, wasn't it?" You can't stop those thoughts from popping up now and then, and you don't have to.

Nor will the cravings for marijuana go away immediately. That's not realistic. But they *will* recede. Quitting marijuana won't require you to resist with all your might for the next ten years. Fortunately, it just doesn't work that way.

I know, right now, you can't imagine ever getting to the point where you don't want to smoke. You will, trust me. You simply have to fully engage the process. First, you have to confront your current reality. You've already been doing that in the first part of this book.

Wouldn't it be nice not to struggle at all? The only way to do that is to eliminate your desire for pot. And the first step to eliminating your desire is changing your beliefs about your "secret addiction."

So we'll turn now to the next step in the process: you have to change your beliefs.

Changing Your Beliefs

"If you are distressed by anything external, the pain is not due to the thing itself, but to your estimate of it; and this you have the power to revoke at any moment."

MARCUS AURELIUS, *MEDITATIONS*

You have to change your beliefs about marijuana. This is crucial to your success. Even though we know many of the negative consequences of smoking, this knowledge is often overridden by the positive benefits we feel we receive, such as relaxation, the ability to cope, being witty or humorous, and an increase in creativity.

This is truly a secret addiction. This is a term I have used mainly because of the general consensus that pot is harmless. There are those who fight tooth and nail to justify its use. It's crazy. We should know better. Maybe it is harmless for those who only occasionally use marijuana, but there are many who started smoking it on a frequent basis and have continued heavy use for a very long time. For such users, it is not harmless! That is not even debatable anymore.

Pot is different than many other substances simply because users can still appear to function, and pot never really allows us to hit "rock-bottom" like other heavier drugs. The phrase that author C.S. Lewis used applies well to marijuana use: "It is a long winding road downhill with not many yield signs." This well describes the slow downward suppression of our capabilities and desires when we allow frequent and heavy smoking to enter our lives.

The truth is that marijuana *never* allows us to rise to the top of our mountain. Yes, there are those who smoke and may seem successful in our eyes. It still doesn't mean they are where they could be. This is dangerous, because some people look to them and think, "If they can do it and have these things, it must be OK." It's not OK, and almost certainly they are not living up to their potential. Neither are we. Deep down we know that.

Those friends who say, "It's only weed," have a serious problem because they are in a state of denial. We must understand that there is more to life than being high, and we must realize these friends have no place in our journey. Those are two beliefs that need to change, if they haven't already. We have to be willing not only to admit those realities, but to embrace them.

Initially, this journey is tough, because everything in your life is changing. Furthermore, we go through so much growth in our teen years and then through our twenties. And, for some of you, most of these growth years have been surrounded by this drug. It will be tough and take a tremendous amount of desire to maintain the will to quit.

However, it does get easier. Around the fourth week you begin to separate yourself from the person you were, and begin to see the reality of the life you have been living. This is not the end, but unlike a foot race, it is much easier at the finish than at the beginning.

I have included a chapter in the book specifically on methods to help your body through the withdrawals. In fact, when I first had the idea for this book, much of the information I was going to write about centered on strategies to help you quit. Sort of a step-by-step manual. However, I realized that until you change your beliefs and gain the correct motivation, then you are more likely headed for another failed attempt to quit. We cannot let that happen. So, this book is about you, as a person, and not just the things you do.

Underlying any potential success is a fundamental change in your beliefs. You must change your beliefs about the drug, and how you abuse it. Isn't it obvious that your justifications are merely a way to obscure the real truth of the matter? They shift your focus from consequence to benefit. This helps to justify continuing on your destructive path despite how it affects you, or those around you.

I was just like you are. A large part of me simply preferred the escape marijuana gave me. Thankfully, it was my family, and my "real life," that weren't too keen on the idea. I came to the point where I started to actually believe that I couldn't keeping smoking marijuana, *and* be a good husband and father, *and* be everything I could be professionally. Those things were simply incompatible. I got to the place where I had to be honest with myself and admit, "I can either be a good husband and dad and doctor, or I can smoke marijuana. I can't do both."

Once that belief changed, I had a choice to make. But the belief had to change first. I had to stop believing I could have my cake and eat it, too. Thinking I could do all of those things was a lie.

We have all heard that "our beliefs create our reality." This includes everything, from our finances to our personal health to our relationships to our attitude toward smoking. Knowing this, the question is whether there is a practical, systematic way to change our beliefs and habits, and therefore our lives.

The good news is there are ways to reprogram our beliefs and our reactions to those beliefs. Is this something that requires consistent repetition? Yes, so that it sinks in. Do we have to go to the extreme of getting up an hour earlier to meditate and visualize our way to a new person? No.

You see, this is where true change helps. It is a subconscious thing; it is automatic. If you are having difficulty with this, then the meditation and visualization techniques explored later in the book do help. But when you really decide to do something, or change your belief about something, you or your brain do not need to be convinced. It is what it is; the truth simply becomes the truth.

But be on watch. Embedded beliefs, or habits, have a way of defending themselves. They defend themselves by leaving you with the feeling that you are doing something wrong, false, useless, pointless, hopeless, or sacrilegious. Sometimes you will hit a plateau where you feel you have made all of the progress you can, and yet the old beliefs still trickle into your mind periodically. Typically, these are the cravings and desires being induced by the many "triggers" in your life.

The most important thing is to not get into an emotional wrestling match with these thoughts. Most people choose to either fight or simply ignore them as they come into their mind. However, after a while, these little thoughts begin to accumulate throughout the day or week, until they start to overcome you. One little thought is not too persuasive, but when they start to wear you down, little by little, you begin to struggle.

This is when it becomes difficult to maintain your resolve. I believe you will find it easier, much easier, to simply recognize the thought when it appears, analyze it without some supercharged emotion, and replace it with the new belief. Sounds silly, but it really does work.

However, the catalyst for this is the initial desire to change the belief itself. Beliefs that you change should be those which are most fundamental. While the desire to eliminate abusive smoking may be the driving force behind wanting to change your current situation, it is likely that fundamental beliefs regarding love, value, self-worth, and fear are ultimately the ones which cause things in your life to be the way they are.

So, changing your beliefs requires knowledge that will empower you. It should empower you about the decisions and choices you make going forward. For that reason, you have to understand the drug you are competing against. Hopefully, this book can provide you with the knowledge to succeed, instead of you idly sitting back and waiting for the feeling to go away. However, understand that knowledge is only a tool. You still have to pick up the hammer and strike the nail!

Changing Your Habits

"The chains of habit are generally too small to be felt until they are too strong to be broken." SAMUEL JOHNSON

Some have heard the advice, from author John Tesh, that it takes about 21 days to establish or break a habit. There is no doubt that changing a habit goes through various stages, and at the one-month mark, it has a markedly different grip on your life. But 21 days might be a bit optimistic for many who are quitting a habit such as smoking. The desire and decision to stop may be there, but habits are routines of behavior that tend to occur subconsciously. In other words, they are automatic. As Frank Crane said, "Habits are safer than rules; you don't have to watch them. And you don't have to keep them, either. They keep you."

Most of life is habitual. You do the same things you did yesterday, the day before, and every day in the past. It is estimated that out of 11,000 signals we receive from our senses, our brain only consciously processes 40. I suppose, in some ways, we are much like robots, whose data has been downloaded by our repetitious behaviors throughout our daily lives.

Habits, good or bad, make us who we are. Just like our actions become habits, our habits become our character. The reason many of you are reading this book is because you know this is not who you are, or who you were intended to be. It no longer serves a purpose in your life, if it ever did at all.

I don't mean to sound pessimistic, but I am trying to establish a reality check. You need to change your habits, and changing habits is not always an easy task. However, people do it all the time. But it takes consistent work. It also takes courage. Only those who desire to change will begin the task. Only those who have the courage will succeed. Courage will keep you on task through the difficult times. Courage will allow you make changes in your life that will be needed for you to win. Courage will be the characteristic that permits you to say "*No!*" when the opportunity to smoke arrives.

Dr. Larry Markson, a friend and mentor, wrote in his book, *Talking to Yourself is not Crazy*, about courage. He says:

> Courage is the answer. I know that sounds too easy, too
> simple and you want me to conjure up some far more exotic
> and complex ingredient. But I assure you there is none. All

that is required is courage and the burning desire to change. It has never been a question of can you change . . . of course you can! It has always been a question of will you change. Well, will you?

Do you have the courage, the guts, the audacity, the tenacity and the determination to shed old habit patterns regardless of how uncomfortable that might be, and persist until new, healthier and more successful habit patterns replace them? That calls for making a major decision. And, by the way, courage is a decision, and no one can give it to you. It cannot be purchased or earned by being nice or by doing good deeds.

Courage is already within you! Perhaps it is dormant, but it is there. Courage comes from you, not to you!

Defined, courage is the state or quality of mind or spirit that enables one to face danger, fear, or vicissitudes with self-possession and bravery. People don't change because they are afraid to change, although after years of trying and failing, their minds now tell them that they are OK the way they are.

It seems as if Dr. Markson wrote that especially for *The Secret Addiction*. Why? Because what it takes to be successful in anything usually takes the same ingredients, the same qualities. If you know how to change your habits, then even a small effort can create big changes. When you defeat this habit, you can defeat anything.

In Part III, we will look at specific steps and techniques you can use to help you break the habit of smoking. For the moment, I want to present several thoughts that prove to be extremely helpful in approaching the whole issue of changing habits.

One Habit at a Time. Changing is a difficult enough process as it is. Trying to tackle multiple bad habits at the same time can easily lead to failure. Change requires focusing on a specific goal at hand. For almost everyone, that means tackling one habit at a time. Choosing to tackle only one at a time doesn't make you weak; it makes you realistic. I hear many people making desperate attempts at quitting cigarettes and marijuana at the same time. I have never smoked cigarettes, but the mere thought of stopping two highly addictive substances simultaneously would drive me insane.

30, 90, 365. Scott Young discusses a series of checkpoints in terms of changing habits:

> The first is at thirty days. Here it doesn't require willpower to continue your change, but problems might offset it. At ninety days any change should be neutral where running the habit is no more difficult than not running it.
>
> At one year it is generally easier not to run the habit than to continue with it. Be patient and run habits through the three checkpoints to make them stick.

It is important to distinguish "habit" versus "craving." The cravings diminish significantly after a short period of time, but it is giving into these habits which re-initiate the cravings to smoke.

Replace Lost Needs. It is very difficult to remove one thing, and not replace it with another. Many of your daily activities surround smoking beforehand. Some of these activities will now just have to be done without smoking, but some of them will need a replacement for the void. An example is finding new ways to relax or socialize. Changing a habit is much easier if you can find other, new habits to adopt in specific circumstances to replace it.

Consistency. It was your consistent, repetitive behavior that created this situation in the first place. It will take the same tenacity and consistent behavior to undo this conditioned response. With enough repetition, you can become anything, or do anything you desire. You were at one time a non-smoker. Isn't it conceivable that you can become a non-smoker again? *You have already done it once before!* Stay consistent and you can win.

At this point, we need to realize that people will approach change with different responses and strategies. Some will be able to follow the advice of Leo Aikman when he said, "The best way to break a bad habit is to drop it." Most, however, will follow the path of Mark Twain when he stated, "Habit is habit, and not to be flung out of the window by any man, but coaxed downstairs a step at a time."

Nevertheless, one thing is consistent from person to person. It is one simple rule you must follow throughout this process. Do not go around telling people you have changed; they will see it for themselves. As author and motivational speaker Richard Flint says, "Behavior never lies!"

PART II

THE NATURE OF THE PROBLEM

Part II of this book is, for the most part, informational. That doesn't mean that it's unimportant. Just the opposite. It's a huge benefit to understand things like whether you are dealing with an addiction or a habit, what type of smoker you are, how exactly THC affects your brain, how smoking pot affects the rest of your body, and if, outside of legitimate medical uses, there are additional benefits to smoking pot. All of these things are vitally important and I highly recommend you read this section.

However, you don't necessarily have to read this book straight through to get maximum benefit from it. If you are ready to commit to quitting smoking, and you want to get started with that process, by all means consider going straight to Part III and get started. If you do that, however, I strongly recommend that once you have started the process, you circle back and read this section. I believe it will prove helpful to your understanding.

If you are not quite ready to commit, this section should help you move toward that point, so keep reading.

CHAPTER 6

Addiction, Habit, or Both?

I've gotten high every day for the last
13 years, thinking that weed is okay to smoke.
I don't think of it as I do other narcotics,
but it sure as hell feels like one when you
want to leave it alone and you can't.

Anonymous

Smokers continue to debate whether the problem we are discussing is simply a bad habit or an addiction. They aren't the
only ones confused. The entire community of drug researchers,
counselors, and authors have been debating this for years. This
chapter won't end the debate, but I will attempt to add some leni-
ency about how you choose to label yourself.

The opponents to the current definition of addiction state that
the term has been confined to a disease model that emphasizes the
biological aspects of the condition while ignoring the psychological,
social, or economic contributors (Peele, 1998). However, common
usage of the term "addiction" has now spread to include psychological dependence. In fact, many medical texts utilize "addiction"

to include a preoccupation with the substance, compulsive use, and frequent relapses (Earlywine, 2002). Sound familiar?

To avoid the social stigma associated with the word "addiction," or to simply be more precise, many mental health professionals prefer to use the more accepted and strictly defined terms of "dependence" and "abuse." These two definitions apply to certain criteria to help the diagnostician place the user into a category based upon the severity of the problem. Dependence is considered the more severe of the two. Both definitions depend upon users' inability to maintain control over their consumption.

Dependence

For an individual to be labeled as "dependent," the user has to show evidence of three of the following seven symptoms:

1. **Tolerance** – This is physiological in nature and something repeated users have all experienced. Simply put, it takes much more marijuana to get the same effect when you are smoking on a frequent basis.

2. **Withdrawal** – Although the symptoms of marijuana withdrawal are dramatically different than other drugs that escape your system at high rate, such as alcohol or heroin, withdrawal is a factor in abstinence. We can debate how much of this effect is psychological and how much is physical, but it is real. If you've tried to abstain before, I don't have to tell you that.

3. **Use that exceeds initial intention** – This applies to those times that you plan on just smoking a small amount, but you find yourself hours later "toking" away, sitting in front of the television, and eating a half gallon of ice cream. Or the times you have an event to attend that evening, so you plan to only

smoke early in the day, but you eventually cancel the event and eat the half gallon of ice cream instead. Whatever the example, our intent is overridden by our lack of control.

4. **Failed attempts to decrease our use or a constant desire for the drug** – No explanation needed. I would not have written this book, nor would you be reading it, if this didn't apply.

5. **Loss of time related to our use** – As Mitch Earlywine stated, "The time lost can be devoted to experiencing intoxication, recovering from it, or seeking it."

6. **Reduced activities** – Again, Earlywine does an excellent job of explaining:

> This symptom focuses on work, relationships, and leisure. The presence of this symptom suggests that the drug has taken over so much of daily life that the user would qualify as dependent. . . . Even with stellar job performance, impaired social functioning can also indicate problems. If a user's only friends are also users, and they only socialize while intoxicated or seeking drugs, the substance has obviously had a marked impact on friendships. Recreational functioning is also important to the diagnosis. A decrease in leisure activities suggests impaired recreation. A smoker who formerly enjoyed hiking, reading, and theater but now spends all free time in front of the television would qualify for the symptom.

7. **Continued use despite problems** – I personally believe this is where our motivation to quit originates. However, despite our recognition of these problems, we persist in our use and ignore the negative consequences to our occupations, social functioning, personal relationships, psychological well-being, and our health. This recognition or awareness

doesn't really go away, even as we continue to smoke. We just get better at ignoring or justifying it. But it continues to resurface and motivates us to try once again.

Abuse

To be placed into the category of "abuse," the user needs only to display *one* of the four symptoms in the following criteria:

1. **Interference with major obligations** – Obviously, some individuals have fewer obligations than others. But we have all put off some obligation we knew we shouldn't, whether it was at school, home, or work, because we got stoned instead.

2. **Intoxication in an unsafe setting** – Driving a car or operating machinery qualifies most people as being in an unsafe setting. Personally, I knew I was a non-functioning smoker, so my activities included as little movement and brain power as possible. But many people continue to believe they function well, or in some cases function better, while intoxicated with weed. One study (Smiley, 1986) even attempted to suggest improved driving with smoking. If any one of you self-proclaimed functional drivers has ever waited for a stop sign to turn green, you have just debunked your own myth of non-impaired driving.

3. **Ignoring the consequences of legal problems** – This simply means the willingness to take the legal risks associated with our desire to smoke. The legal landscape concerning marijuana is changing rapidly, of course. As of November 2020, 15 states had legalized it, 13 states have decriminalized it and provide for legal medical use, 14 states provide for only legal medical use, 2 states have only decriminalized it, and all use is still illegal in 6 states. Worldwide, marijuana use

is still illegal in most countries. Regardless of whether you think marijuana use should be legal or not, in many places it still carries legal consequences.

4. **Continued use despite problems** – This is identical to the definition we found in the discussion of "dependence." However, it is important enough to place in both categories. Hmmm, I wonder why?

By now, most of you have realized that you may belong to all three of these definitions: addiction, dependence, and abuse. I know I did. My suggestion is to pick your poison, whatever word you feel comfortable with or whichever seems to apply more appropriately. The bottom line is that you have a problem, and the problem is more important than the label. Right? One author poignantly stated, "Instead of worrying about whether a specific user qualifies for a disorder, time might be better spent identifying individual problems related to marijuana use."

Personally, I tend to use the three words interchangeably. When I use the word "habit" instead of "addiction," I am not attempting in any way to minimize the problem. Whatever you want to call it, the problem needs fixing.

Psychological or Physical?

"People always seem relieved to hear that a substance 'just' produces a psychological addiction, or has only minimal physical withdrawal symptoms. Then they discount its dangers. They are wrong. Marijuana is a case in point here."

ALAN I. LESHNER, PH.D., DIRECTOR, NIDA

Many people make the argument that marijuana is only psychologically addicting, not physically addicting. At least they acknowledge that the drug *is* addicting. But their argument misses the point. Trying to lessen the problem by stating it is a mere psychological, or mental addiction, is a poor argument.

Why? First, because marijuana is clearly physically addicting. When we speak of physical addictions, we typically are referring to the dramatic physical withdrawal symptoms that occur when an individual stops taking a drug. Countless discussions with people who have attempted to seriously quit marijuana and many studies indicate the definite physical component to marijuana withdrawal. It may be milder than someone getting off of heroin or alcohol, but it does exist.

More importantly, to minimize the problem by brushing it off as a simple psychological addiction betrays a misunderstanding of addiction. Alan Leshner of the National Institute of Drug Abuse explains:

> Focusing on this physical vs. psychological distinction is off the mark, and a distraction from the real issue. From both clinical and policy perspectives, it does not matter much what physical withdrawal symptoms occur. Other aspects of addiction are far more important.
>
> What does matter tremendously is whether or not a drug causes what we now know to be the essence of addiction: uncontrollable, compulsive drug seeking and use, even in the face of negative health and social consequences. This is the crux of how many professional organizations all define addiction, and how we all should use the term. It is really only this expression of addiction—uncontrollable, compulsive craving, seeking and use of drugs—that matters to the addict and to his or her family, and that should matter to society as a whole. These are the elements responsible for the massive health and social problems caused by drug addiction.

Drug craving and the other compulsive behaviors are the essence of addiction. They are extremely difficult to control, much more difficult than any physical dependence. But what matters much more is that every year more than 100,000 people, most of them adolescents, seek treatment for their inability to control their marijuana use. They suffer from compulsive, uncontrollable marijuana craving, seeking and use. That makes it addicting, certainly for a large number of people.

Chronic smokers who say pot is "just" psychologically addictive are implying that since it is a mental thing, they can quit when they want. We have all told ourselves that at one time, haven't we? Maybe you are still telling yourself that. Fine. Then quit. If you're so strong mentally, just quit. It's as simple as that.

But we don't quit. We set timelines or goals for the day we are going to stop, whether it be when we have a future job, or have a child, or when we reach a certain age. But those times come and pass, and we, once again, reset our timeline for stopping.

People whose primary drug of abuse is marijuana consider themselves different than other drug users. Potheads even feel that they are a different breed when compared to the alcoholic. Believe me, if someone was addicted to harder drugs such as heroin or crack, they wouldn't be reading this book. They have other problems that need to be addressed first. But when dealing with compulsive drug addictions, it's pretty much the same regardless of the drug. The dependence always stems from both a psychological and physical origin. Maybe the emphasis in one area might be greater than the other, but denying one or the other is to deny the appropriate recovery strategy.

There is no doubt concerning the physiological reaction that the body has to stopping marijuana. How can we deny it? But all physical withdrawal symptoms do come to an end. For marijuana, it takes about one month to completely eliminate all of the physical part. Furthermore, there are many things you can do to help with the effects of getting the drug out of your system. These are detailed in chapters 20 and 21. However, it's not the physical component of this addiction that gives marijuana the highest failure rate of abstinence among illegal (or recently illegal) drugs; it's the psychological.

The psychological component will produce drug cravings and relapses months after being away from the drug. This is the reason you need to take abstinence seriously. You have to abandon the notion that after abstaining for one month, or following this book's advice for the next 45 days, you will be completely over your dependence.

I am not in any way ascribing to the "disease" theory of addiction. Your problem with marijuana is not a part of you in the same way as if you had leprosy. You shouldn't have to live "one day at a time" in fear that today might be your relapse day. That gives the addiction too much power over you. Sure, initially, it has a tremendous amount of power. That's why you have smoked for so long. However, it does get very easy *once you have made a change in you*. When you do, that old part of you, the pot-smoking part, will eventually disappear.

✎ PERSONAL TASK #4

Cannabis Use Disorder Identification Test – Revised (CUDIT-R)

Various assessments have been developed to determine if a person's marijuana smoking is causing problems in his life, regardless of what label we attach to it. That is, after all, the main issue—is this activity causing serious problems in my life?

One of these assessments is the Cannabis Use Disorder Identification Test – Revised (CUDIT-R). Take this brief test now.

Cannabis Use Disorder Identification Test – Revised (CUDIT-R)

Have you used any cannabis over the past six months?　　YES / NO

If YES, please answer the following questions about your cannabis use.

Circle the response that is most correct for you in relation to your cannabis use *over the past six months.*

1. How often do you use cannabis?

Never	Monthly or less	2-4 times a month	2-3 times a week	4 or more times a week
0	1	2	3	4

2. How many hours were you "stoned" on a typical day when you had been using cannabis?

Less than 1	1 or 2	3 or 4	5 or 6	7 or more
0	1	2	3	4

3. How often during the past 6 months did you find that you were not able to stop using cannabis once you had started?

Never	Less than monthly	Monthly	Weekly	Daily or almost daily
0	1	2	3	4

4. How often during the past 6 months did you fail to do what was normally expected from you because of using cannabis?

Never	Less than monthly	Monthly	Weekly	Daily or almost daily
0	1	2	3	4

Cannabis Use Disorder Identification Test – Revised (CUDIT-R)

5. How often in the past 6 months have you devoted a great deal of your time to getting, using, or recovering from cannabis?

Never	Less than monthly	Monthly	Weekly	Daily or almost daily
0	1	2	3	4

6. How often in the past 6 months have you had a problem with your memory or concentration after using cannabis?

Never	Less than monthly	Monthly	Weekly	Daily or almost daily
0	1	2	3	4

7. How often do you use cannabis in situations that could be physically hazardous, such as driving, operating machinery, or caring for children?

Never	Less than monthly	Monthly	Weekly	Daily or almost daily
0	1	2	3	4

8. Have you ever thought about cutting down, or stopping, your use of cannabis?

Never	Yes, but not in the past 6 months	Yes, during the past 6 months
0	2	4

This scale is in the public domain and is free to use with appropriate citation:
Adamson SJ, Kay-Lambkin FJ, Baker AL, Lewin TJ, Thornton L. Kelly BJ, and Sellman JD. (2010). An improved Brief Measure of Cannabis Misuse: The Cannabis Use Disorders Identification Test – Revised (CUDIT-R). *Drug and Alcohol Dependence* 110:137-143.

This questionnaire was designed for self administration and is scored by adding each of the 8 items:
 – Questions 1-7 are scored on a 0-4 scale.
 – Question 8 is scored 0, 2 or 4.

Scores of 8 or more indicate hazardous cannabis use, while scores of 12 or more indicate a possible cannabis use disorder for which further intervention may be required.

CHAPTER 7

Three Types of Smokers

I've always, how you say, 'maintained' when I was high. I wouldn't turn into a giggling mess like some of my comrades, and this gave me confidence . . . the confidence to smoke more often because I could control it. I could function, and do the more or less "brainless" work involved in my studies, but I could never manage to take my skills to the next level. I just wouldn't absorb the information. But I'd never blame the reefer . . . even though I knew it was the problem.

Anonymous

Everyone has a reason why he or she smokes. When you look at all the reasons given by most smokers, though, they can be placed into three categories: the social smoker, the psychological smoker, and the stress smoker. Of course, these overlap. No one is purely one and not the other two. But it's important to understand what type of smoker you are so you can better resolve the underlying conditions that will prompt you to smoke again when the going gets tough.

One category of smokers that I will not include in this chapter is the individual with a legitimately diagnosed medical condition. As of this writing, 42 states have legalized medical use of marijuana (some states, of course, have legalized it completely). Humans have used marijuana for medicinal purposes for millennia, and without a doubt it can provide some benefits to some people, particularly in the area of pain management with various diseases, such as some cancers, multiple sclerosis, etc.

The flip side, of course, is that some people are using medicine simply as an excuse to smoke, even when their medical condition is more tolerable than they admit, or when there are better alternatives to correct or manage it.

The Social Smoker

Social smoking is how most people get their first experience of smoking marijuana. Whether it is just curiosity or whether you happen to be at the wrong place at the wrong time, it usually starts with a group of friends hanging out, and with one of the members having some pot.

This first experience can go one of three ways. First, your initial toke scared the crap out of you for whatever reason and you swore that you would never smoke it again. Secondly, it's not really that big of a deal, and you can take it or leave it. Besides, your mouth was so dry that your tongue felt like it was the size of your foot, and standing up seemed as if someone had super glued the couch to your rear when you weren't paying attention.

The third reaction, however, is the one that often begins the captivation with marijuana, and sets the stage for a life of daily smoking. It was just plain fun! No matter what you were doing, and who you were with, everything just seemed better. Things appeared funnier than usual. Even typically shy or soft-spoken you turned into somewhat of a comedian. The movies you watched, if you were able to stay awake, were more action-packed, colorful, or hilarious. The cookies you ate were the most delicious pack of stale cookies you had ever eaten. Any music you listened to, whether your own or someone else's, just sounded that much better.

We know these heightened experiences are simply how pot works on your brain, but it is enough to send you back chasing that experience once again. And this is where it all begins.

Obviously, this is not like the story of a crack-cocaine abuser who after the first hit knew he was hooked. Pot is different than that. It is much more subtle and, therefore, the habit can sneak up on you. It's the seemingly harmless repetition over time that becomes the enemy. You are simply trying to enjoy life through the haze of a smoke-filled room when, one day, you wake up to a lifestyle that revolves around getting high in order to enjoy anything.

That's when it becomes "the secret addiction." It is so ingrained in your daily routine that in order to break free of the chains, you have to change the way you experience life. It's not that you have to change everything about your routines, hobbies, etc. You just have to learn to do them without the pot.

It sounds really difficult, doesn't it? Or maybe it just sounds a little boring. Trust me when I tell you that it is neither too difficult nor boring. You just have to be willing to do these things without the pot. It's as simple as that. Believe it or not, movies are still great to watch, but now you can actually remember them. Music is still great to listen to or even create. Food is still wonderful to eat, but now you will not have to pay for the repercussions of eating four servings, instead of just one.

Now, do not think I am naïve enough to believe that doing these things, when you are high, isn't fun. I wouldn't have smoked for almost a decade if I didn't enjoy that part. Any person who smokes regularly would be lying if they said that. The point I am making is that this smoking habit has interfered with your life in other ways and any pleasure you have while doing things high is not worth the agony you go through as a whole.

Learning to live life in a normal state of mind is still enjoyable and worth living. How do we know this? Because people are doing it all the time. Even though it may seem to you like a lot of people smoke weed regularly, it is actually a small minority of individuals who do.

The Psychological Smoker

The psychological smoker introduces a different set of issues to deal with. Someone suffering from a true psychological condition, such as severe depression, schizophrenia, or some other form of psychosis, should not attempt to break the habit alone. There are too many risks associated with a severe psychological disorder, and you need to be under the guidance of a healthcare provider who understands and has experience in dealing with these types of conditions.

There are many people who may be dealing with less severe psychological issues, such as mild depression or even poor anger management skills. When you are smoking, these problems seem to disappear. On the other hand, when you try to quit, these mild problems seem to surface as larger problems than previously thought. There can be several reasons why, but the main reason is due to the fact that you have never learned how to cope with these feelings.

Because the withdrawals you go through whenever you try to stop smoking can put anyone in a bad or a "less-than-happy" mood, you have a tendency to run back to the same thing you are trying to escape. In the face of bad feelings, our willpower seems to crumble, because our immediate felt need is to escape from the bad feelings.

An interesting question is whether or not marijuana can actually worsen the underlying psychological condition. A 2008 report on teen marijuana use and depression released by the Office of National Drug Control Policy stated:

> Recent studies show that marijuana and depression are a
> dangerous combination. In fact, using marijuana can worsen
> depression and lead to more serious mental health disorders,
> such as schizophrenia, anxiety, and even suicide. Weekly
> or more frequent use of marijuana doubles a teen's risk of
> depression and anxiety. Depressed teens are more than
> twice as likely as their peers to abuse, or become dependent
> on marijuana.

In an address to The Royal College of General Practitioners, the UK's professional body for general practicing physicians, Dr. Clare Gerada said that greater acceptance of marijuana and greater availability of stronger forms of it were leading to rising rates of depression, psychosis and schizophrenia. She noted, "There is clear evidence that high levels of use, especially among teenagers who are physically and mentally still developing, carries with it the increased risk of psychosis and respiratory conditions such as asthma."

The bottom line is that marijuana and psychological issues make for a complicated mix—usually not a healthy one. To repeat, if you are suffering from or have a history of a severe psychological condition, you need someone who can help you co-manage this and your desired abstinence at the same time. Conversely, if the issues you deal with are in the less severe category, there are many ways to manage your mood or your anger. These suggestions are clearly laid out for you in other chapters throughout the book. The responsibility now lies with you to utilize them to your advantage.

The Stress Smoker

"Although many factors can contribute to initial and continued drug use, exposure to either psychological or physiological stress at any point in the addiction cycle seems to worsen this disease, augmenting all drug seeking behaviors, including initial drug taking, drug craving, and relapse."

JESSICA N. CLECK AND JULIE A. BLENDY

The most common reason people light up on a daily basis is stress. The need to simply "unwind" from a busy day, or the need to escape a situation in life, leads people to continue with an addictive habit. I know from experience that even in the most extreme cases of stress, you do not have to depend on marijuana as a way to escape. There are other, healthier ways to cope. We simply have to learn them and put them into practice.

The *Brief Counseling for Marijuana Dependence* manual captures why people develop a marijuana habit as a way to cope with stress:

Marijuana dependence is considered a learned behavior developed in response to external (e.g., environmental, relational, occupational) and internal conditions (e.g., feelings, thoughts). The addictive behavior has become a favored strategy, because of its repeated associations with predictable outcomes. For example, someone uses marijuana when he or she is sad, angry, lonely, or upset. He or she feels less bad when smoking and associates marijuana use with feeling better, at least in the short term. Over time, marijuana may be used more often as a strategy to escape negative feelings or thoughts.

Marijuana dependence is a habit caused by repetition. Some of you are so hard on yourself that the self-esteem and confidence needed to conquer this problem is wavering somewhere in the distance. It doesn't need to be. Any habit that has been learned can be un-learned.

Most people do not start out as a "stress smoker." Many have already had an experience with marijuana, usually as a social smoker and are familiar with the effects. Does this point to the possibility that coping skills, and stress or anger management skills, were lacking prior to the problem? Does this strengthen the argument that these skills need to be improved? Absolutely! This book covers many of these topics in more detail, but, more importantly, you are a continuing work in progress and will need to constantly improve in these areas, even after you have overcome this part of your life.

There is an acronym used for people who trying to manage their stress in healthy ways. The acronym is H-A-L-T, which stands for:

H – Don't allow yourself to get too hungry. We just don't think straight when we're too hungry.

A – Don't allow yourself to become too angry. Isn't this a major reason why many people return to smoking? In fact, it is so important that I have dedicated part of Chapter 15 to various strategies for dealing with anger.

L – Don't allow yourself to become too isolated and lonely. Boredom and loneliness rank up there with anger. Either you have isolated yourself from friends and family who are non-smokers and have become anti-social, or you have forgotten how to participate in activities that do not include smoking. Too many people passively wait for things to change, but you are responsible for making that change.

T – Don't allow yourself to become too tired. Tiredness or fatigue can easily lead to stress, poor sleeping habits, etc. Try to take it as easy as possible during the beginning stages and avoid this problem.

In an article called "The Stressed Smoking Myth," Dr. Daniel Seidman speaks of people's desire for cigarettes when dealing with stress. It almost seems as if Dr. Seidman wrote this piece specifically for marijuana abusers. I changed a few of his words to fit marijuana smokers:

> Many smokers share the common belief, "I need [weed] because I am stressed. I need this to cope with stress." You may really believe this and, like so many smokers, this is how you explain your smoking behavior to yourself. But what if it's just a belief, not a fact?
>
> What if smoking is just an overrated activity . . . a bad habit . . . a routine, negative behavior having nothing to do with stress management? Perhaps it distracts you when you're upset. But can smoking solve real-life problems? No, it is a real-life problem itself. This is the classic false belief of addicted smokers, and it must be challenged and debunked to learn to live smoke-free.
>
> Smoking because of stress is what is called a rationalization. This is something you tell yourself to try to make yourself feel good about something you really feel bad about. We all do it, but smokers are especially prone to rationalize about stress and smoking. The truth is that an addicted smoker doesn't need a reason to smoke. The momentum of smoking, its automatic quality, is a three-headed monster. It comes from:
>
> - The effect that smoking [weed] has on your brain and body
> - The repetitive, habitual nature of smoking
> - The role of the smoker's social environment— primarily exposure to other smokers and smoke, which are contagious
>
> Smoking is an uncreative, and repetitive response, to life stress. It actually weakens the opportunity to develop healthy and flexible coping responses by relying on a fixed and irresponsible way of responding to living.

Stress is the most common reason people light up every day. Many people seem to have very good reasons, at times, why they smoke. But it's a lot more complicated than that. If the research is correct, then chronic drug use can alter the brains of users, causing them to respond very differently to stress than individuals who are not habitual smokers. In essence, coping mechanisms are neurologically changed into a more negative psychological and physiological response. In other words, we become weak and unable to handle what most people cope with day in and day out.

Furthermore, psychological stress has also been shown to induce drug taking behaviors. So not only is the stress magnified, but we are now more prone to turn to the drug to deal with the situation. As I have said before, coping and managing the problems in your life are two different things.

Simply coping with the trials in our lives does nothing to improve the situation. It is true that some problems do go away on their own accord. But some will linger and haunt you, and may drive you into a vicious cycle of stress smoking that will leave you suffocating in a bellow of smoke and unable to see any solution even if it were two feet in front of you.

Trust me. No matter what you think you can't deal with sober, you can. It will not kill you. I am sure you know someone who has gone through an ordeal you would not wish upon anyone. But somehow they made it, without marijuana. The smoking, however, will prevent you from taking the necessary action you need to solve the challenges you face. Whether you have to deal with problems emotionally or physically, you cannot afford to sit in a daze playing video games or watching TV and expect your problems to disappear.

What if your problems are directly related to the smoking? Then obviously, this stuff is messing up your life. Isn't it odd that the very root of the problem is what you are using to address the problem that it created in the first place? That sounds crazy. If you were vomiting (problem) because of a poison (marijuana), you wouldn't drink the poison to stop the vomiting, would you? Of course not! The smartest way to stop the problem is to quit drinking the poison.

I am not suggesting that dealing with uncomfortable situations is an easy task. Nothing associated with kicking a habit is easy. But you need to learn how to cope with life's tough situations. People do it all the time, and you can too. After a few good twists in the road, you will get the hang of it. You did it before you started smoking, didn't you?

In Conclusion

Many people, at some level, can relate to all three categories: social smoking, psychological smoking, and stress smoking. This may sound as if you have a lot of work to do. Learning to deal with new stress coping skills, while changing your friends and habits, sounds a bit challenging, and it is to a degree. But when you stop smoking and your dependence begins to weaken, you can naturally handle things differently, and your activities and friends change as well. There are parts of the change process that we fear, such as the loss of our social networks, or not being able to perform or enjoy parts of our life, that, once we start making changes, are not as difficult as we might expect.

The change at the beginning of the process is simply change. Any alteration in the normal patterns of how we do anything can seem a bit uncomfortable. Whether it is the time that you get up in the morning, a new job, or a change in eating habits, we eventually get used to the new routine and become more comfortable. It is no longer change, but just who we are, and how we are living our life at that moment.

CHAPTER 8

Understanding Pot

My "pros and cons" list of why I smoke is often
fairly balanced, but lately I figure it's just
balancing what it messed up in the first place.

Anonymous

This book does not present a "fair and balanced" view of marijuana smoking. My intention is not to get into the debate over whether legalization is a good thing, and I certainly have no intention of exciting either the pro- or anti-marijuana circles. Whether marijuana is legal or not is mostly irrelevant to this book. If anyone really wants to research the benefits vs. the consequences of chronic smoking, I know what they will find, and it won't be very positive.

I have written this book because the fact is that there are millions of individuals who are currently making, and will in the future be making, an attempt to get away from this habit. Those that have already made the effort recognize how daunting this task can be, and how little information is available for those wanting to quit.

The people reading this book for its intended purpose aren't interested in a debate as to whether it is good or bad to smoke. For them, it has gotten out of control and interfered with their life in many ways, and this seems to be something that many chronic smokers, who continue to smoke, do not *yet* understand. Although some have had brief moments of considering the possibility of stopping, they typically wait until the feeling goes away, or they somehow convince themselves it is OK to live their life in a fog of passivity with some lame excuse or reasoning.

It sounds as if I am being a little harsh, doesn't it? Not really. It is simply the truth. When you hear logic such as, "Why would God put this on the earth if he didn't want us to smoke it?" or "It's just a plant, so it's natural," be honest with yourself for a moment. Do you really think those are valid statements that you can defend? The argument that marijuana is natural is common. I can think of a thousand things that are natural, but that doesn't mean they were intended for me to roll them up in a piece of paper, light it, and fill my lungs with toxic smoke and chemicals. Did nature really intend for us to have smoke in our lungs?

There are people who smoke purely for medical reasons, such as to dull the agony of a terminal cancer or the pain induced by multiple sclerosis. This book is not for them. My heart goes out to them, and I pray for all the best for them as they go through a very difficult experience. The fact is that marijuana has been used for medicinal purposes as far back as 2700 B.C. Some medicinal uses of marijuana over the centuries may have been unfounded, but many of its uses are valid. In some cases, it is a better alternative compared to many of the treatments and drugs used today in modern medicine.

However, warnings of its abuse have usually not traveled far behind. As Mitch Earlywine stated in his book *Understanding Marijuana: A New Look at the Scientific Evidence,* "the story of cannabis as a medicine is separate from its role as a recreational drug."

There are some who claim to be "therapeutic" users, but the illnesses they have are easily treatable with other methods. Furthermore, many who smoke or use other opiate types of drugs, like pain medication, often exaggerate conditions or symptoms to justify or continue the drug for its intoxicating effects. This requires a reality check on the part of the user!

Many people who use marijuana for what they say are medical reasons have never even seen a doctor or have never attempted to address the problem in any other way. They continue to sleepwalk through life and avoid the discomfort of trying to overcome whatever ailment is holding them captive. Emotional scars have left some of you without an ounce of self-esteem or hope. No matter what has happened in your past, you can overcome this. It will take pigheaded discipline, but I know you can do it.

In addition, this book is not for those who honestly believe they do not have any problems with smoking, and that it causes no interference in their daily life. I have friends who smoke regularly and are the happiest and most content people you will ever meet. However, there are many of you striving to quit this merry-go-round, and you should not be ridiculed for this decision by those people who are comfortable with continuing to smoke on a periodic or daily basis. This book is intended to help those who are ready to make a change.

This chapter will address some of the false claims about marijuana given by both pro-marijuana and anti-marijuana groups. Many of the false claims, or those attached to flawed research, have been used by the pro-marijuana groups as ammunition for its legalization, or for justifying its use. There are numerous studies we can cite that point to the adverse effects of abusive smoking. Numerous others are surfacing as we learn more about this drug.

It is important to utilize the research, when necessary, but it is not the only tool we have. Personal experience leads to a greater awareness of the truth of the problem. Let's face it: most users are not worried about changes to their sperm, or the gateway effect to other drugs. They are just tired of the grip smoking has on them, and they want to stop.

Some people might argue that I (Tony) "have just forgotten what it's like to be a stoner." This is ludicrous. You never forget what it's like to abuse a drug, and the many disappointments you create along the way. I will continue to say what I know is right concerning this addiction, because my heart's desire is to help people improve their lives. "Mary Jane" has stolen what could be years of productive living from millions of individuals. I want to help people turn that around and start living to the full. It's doable. I know that from personal experience.

So, if it seems like I come across from time to time as bashing "Mary Jane," I'm not sorry. You are more important to me than she is. Besides, she has many other friends out there who will continue to defend her.

Know Your Stuff

"For the longest time I knew I had a problem, but was always afraid to reach out. I thought people would say things like, 'It's only weed man. How can you have a problem with that?' I have felt that it has always been a horrible injustice that marijuana abuse hasn't been taken more seriously. There are those of us who have had real problems and have felt as if there was nowhere to turn." ROBIN T.

Since you are seeking to end your dependence on a certain drug, it helps to understand more about that drug than simply how to grow, roll, or prepare it. This chapter is intended to provide more context for your decision to quit marijuana and start a brand new, healthier chapter in your life.

Whoa, That's a Lot of Pot!

It's difficult to accurately estimate the number of smokers, due to the reluctance of people to confess illegal behavior. Estimating the amounts that individuals smoke is an equal challenge because of the irregularity of the range of potencies and individuals' tendency to exaggerate, minimize, or simply not remember the amounts they consume.

However, some researchers have estimated that there are a whopping 200 to 300 million people who smoke marijuana worldwide. Other surveys have indicated that approximately 4.3 million Americans smoke on a daily basis, and approximately one-third of U.S. adults have smoked marijuana at least once. The UN Office on Drugs and Crime indicates that in 2006-2007 some 166 million people aged 15 to 64, or 3.9 per cent of the world's population in this age group, used it regularly.

These numbers are staggering, particularly since much of the information in these surveys come from individuals who are willing to admit their usage. By some estimates, Americans alone are smoking 3.5 to 4.5 million pounds of marijuana per year. These numbers are probably similar in most other industrialized countries.

Even if only 1% of the people in the world smoked regularly, that would equate to over 70 million people. The bottom line is that there are more people abusing marijuana than any other drug, with the exception of alcohol and cigarettes. Given the fact that I have met very few frequent smokers who have not contemplated quitting at some time during their smoking career, I estimate there are millions of people trying to escape the bondage that cannabis has them in. One study of more than 42,000 participants, who had smoked in the previous year, concluded that 6% to 23% had some form of difficulty with the drug.

Chemical Make-up and Potency

Marijuana has approximately 420 different chemical compounds, of which about 60 are called cannabinoids. From an addictive standpoint, the most important and examined compound is delta-9 tetrahydrocannabinol (THC), which gives marijuana most of its psychoactive effects. THC is also used to indicate the potency of the preparation (in percentage). Two other compounds, cannabinol and cannabidiol, have been given considerable attention lately as our understanding of the drug increases.

There are many different forms and ways of ingesting these cannabinoids, such as marijuana, hashish, hash oil, and synthetic medications like dronabinol (Marinol). Hashish, or hash for short, typically contains 20% THC with its counterpart, hash oil, potentially containing an overwhelming 70%. However, most pot smokers have never come in contact with hash or its oil. The vast majority of smokers around the world still use marijuana as the common way of getting THC into their system. Marijuana usually consists of 2 to 5% THC, but may be as high as 20% or more.

Marijuana is lipophilic, meaning it is soluble (stored) in fat, which makes it insoluble in water. Since THC is stored in fatty tissue and is slowly excreted through the body for elimination, it can be detected long after use. Detection usually ranges from 12-13 days, and up to 30 days for some individuals. Although the THC stored in fat is not in amounts that can produce psychoactive effects, excretion could lead some individuals to crave the drug as it travels through the system. Many people are in such a hurry to eliminate the drug from their system when they quit that they will use various methods to speed up the detoxification process. However, this may not be such a good idea.

Research indicates that marijuana is currently much more potent than it was in the 60s and 70s. According to the Marijuana Monitoring Project (Madrigal, 2008), average THC levels of cannabis in the US market almost doubled between 1999 and 2006, from 4.6% to 8.8%. This was due to a shift in indoor production of higher potency strains. The latest figure from the Department of Justice's National Drug Intelligence Center indicate potency has tripled since 1987.

Does any of this potency controversy really matter? Although the evidence clearly indicates there has been an increase in potency since the 60s, the most important issue is that some people are having problems abstaining from a drug that is having a negative impact on in their lives.

The Gateway Controversy

Whether or not marijuana is a "gateway drug" (that is, does it lead to the use of and addiction to heavier drugs) is still a hotly debated issue. I understand a parent's concern, after finding some pot stashed away in a sock drawer, that their kid might be prone to moving onto heavier drugs. And they might be right. Some people contend that marijuana was the culprit leading them into the grips of cocaine, ecstasy, or crack. However, this is difficult to prove and, in my opinion, is not addressing the main question. The problem is not with marijuana, as much as it is with the person. Is this a person who is trying to find their meaning in life, or escape from problems in life, by using drugs? That is the real issue. Speaking personally, the only gateway effect I experienced was overeating, which is a link that can definitely be proven.

When all marijuana use was illegal, it could reasonably be argued that individuals who were willing to use one illegal substance were probably willing to experiment with others. Because they were all illegal, marijuana and other drugs were only available on the black market, and anyone who entered the drug market was likely to be exposed to more than one drug. For someone to be exposed to marijuana meant they were around friends, relatives, or dealers who had access to or participated in other illegal substances. I think it was probably the exposure and willingness to participate that was the main problem, not some automatic progression from marijuana to crack.

So many states have legalized or decriminalized marijuana by now, of course, that this is less of an issue. In states where you can drive down to the local pot shop, obtaining marijuana doesn't expose you to anything except maybe bad traffic. Of course, that doesn't mean marijuana is harmless. But you've already discovered that in your own life, or you wouldn't be halfway through this book.

In states where marijuana is still illegal, of course, all of the analysis above still applies.

Many pot smokers are unique in that they do not use or abuse any other substances other than nicotine. In fact, I have heard many potheads use this as one of the justifications for making their weed addiction acceptable. But the fact that you don't drink alcohol or use other drugs is a poor reason to smoke weed on a regular basis.

Whether or not marijuana is a gateway drug has no impact on what we know for sure about its own negative effects. Studies have indicated that about 9% up to 21% of regular users can be classified as dependent (Swift et al., 2001, Anthony et al., 1994). In addition, respiratory and lung cancer risks are raised for cannabis users, and damage to verbal learning ability, memory, and attention can occur. Studies have indicated changes in receptors of the hippocampus, prefrontal cortex, cerebellum, and other parts of the brain in heavy cannabis users. There is also the potential for increases in psychosis and other disorders, such as schizophrenia. Research has also indicated links between early cannabis use and poor school performance.

Marijuana and the Lungs

"Chemically, marijuana and tobacco smoke are quite similar, aside from their psychoactive ingredients: both arise from the combustion of leafy material, which produces a host of noxious

gases and solid particulates, or tars that are known to be hazardous to respiratory health." DALE GIERINGER, PH.D.

Of the many deleterious effects of smoking marijuana, lung impairment is one that is hard to debate. Even the most ardent pro-marijuana supporters usually won't deny this issue.

Marijuana absolutely has an impact on the lungs. That's a fact. How can igniting with a butane lighter a leafy substance rolled in paper and sucking the smoke deep into the lungs not be harmful? Oh, you're not using paper, or you're using a different way to ignite it? Let's you and me go run a mile together and see what vile stuff comes flying out of your lungs.

Oxygen and blood are the main substances intended to be traveling through our lungs, not smoke. There is nothing natural about smoke in our lungs. You can argue that there are devices to minimize the chemicals, such as a vaporizer, but the majority of people will never use one of these because of the expense, or it just isn't "the same."

It's important to get our facts straight. You may have heard that smoking a marijuana cigarette is equivalent to smoking 20 regular cigarettes. This simply is not true. However, that doesn't mean that a marijuana cigarette is harmless. It is still worse in some respects than a regular tobacco cigarette. For instance, marijuana smokers absorb four times as much tar in their lungs as do cigarette smokers (Wu et al., 1988). Other researchers have shown that for measures of airflow obstruction, one cannabis joint had a similar effect as 2.5 to 5 tobacco cigarettes (Aldington et al., 2007).

Breathing

I would say the ability to breathe effectively is pretty important, wouldn't you? Several studies I reviewed showed the effect that smoking marijuana had on what is called "forced expiratory volume," or FEV. FEV is basically measured by how much air an individual can force out of their lungs in one second. The less you can force out, the less overall lung capacity you have. Researchers have shown a decrease in FEV with smoking marijuana, and it gets worse with heavier use (Taylor et al., 2002). Can you imagine the effect of smoking for thirty years?

In addition, the result is magnified when you smoke both marijuana and tobacco, which many users do. However, many people are completely unaware of the impact, simply because they do nothing to stress their lungs. But if you were to run up and down a flight of stairs a few times, or run around the block, you would certainly notice the effect.

Just simple everyday breathing doesn't take a tremendous amount of effort, for now.

That's the problem with smoking anything. It takes so long to experience major side-effects that by the time they show up, *it's too late*. For most people, there is too much elapsed time between being healthy and being sick. Since the symptoms from smoking are not immediately evident, we feel we are free to continue our destructive behavior.

Additional Symptoms

Does marijuana cause other respiratory disorders? It does not appear to cause emphysema, a disorder that occurs in the lower lungs and smaller airways which marijuana smoke does not typically affect. However, Dr. Tashkin's work indicates that heavy daily marijuana smokers are more susceptible than non-marijuana smokers to several other respiratory disorders, such as coughing, bronchitis, and impaired lung immune function (Tashkin, 1993). Other symptoms include wheezing (apart from colds), exercise-induced shortness of breath, nocturnal wakening with chest tightness and early morning sputum production.

Phlegm and the Healing Process

The good news is that, as far as the damage to the lungs is concerned, most of it is repairable (as with the cilia), and the lungs will increasingly function more effectively over the first year of non-smoking.

The downside of this, from an experiential standpoint, is the excess production of phlegm. When the smoking stops, excess phlegm production begins. When will it stop? This is a question I receive quite frequently. Phlegm usually starts around the second day and will continue for about a month or more with heavy smokers. This, in a strange way, is a good feeling, because your lungs are now able to do what they have been wanting to do for years, but the tar (among other things) was smothering the cilia that moves debris out of the lining of the lung.

It is very effective to help this process along with exercise and drinking water. A product that is extremely beneficial is N-Acetyl Cysteine (NAC). NAC is an anti-mucosal, and will, therefore, help thin the mucus for you. The dosages are covered in Chapter 20.

Cancer

Cancer from smoking marijuana is a more hotly debated topic. In the past, studies have been very limited, and in some cases, merely speculative. Nevertheless, a quick search on lung cancer and cannabis use uncovers some disturbing reports. Recent research has been much clearer on the subject, and speculation is quickly becoming a thing of the past.

For years many pro-marijuana websites and adherents flaunted the results of a 2006 study by researcher and pulmonologist, Dr. Donald Tashkin, which showed no association between marijuana use and the development of lung cancer. This differed from previous conclusions his studies had reached over the previous thirty years.

As testing procedures improved and equipment became more sophisticated, however, we could more easily detect the potential cancer-causing effects of heavy marijuana use in relation to lung cancer. Research carried out by Raj Singh and published in *Chemical Research in Toxicology* in 2009 described the development and use of a modified mass spectrometry method which showed clear indications that marijuana smoke damages DNA. The article cited on *Science Daily's* website stated:

> These results provide evidence for the DNA-damaging potential of cannabis [marijuana] smoke, implying that the consumption of cannabis cigarettes may be detrimental to human health with the possibility to initiate cancer development.

Another study, published in the *European Respiratory Journal* in 2008, showed a clear association between marijuana use and lung cancer. In fact, this study indicated an 8% increase in the chance of developing cancer per year of smoking marijuana. These researchers also noted several other facets induced by smoking, such as:

- One joint is similar to 20 cigarettes for the risk of lung cancer.
- A "few" cannabis joints cause the same tissue changes in the tissue of the throat and lungs as 20-30 cigarettes per day.
- Smoking two joints creates changes in sputum cells (mucus from the trachea or bronchi) similar to 30 cigarettes per day.
- One joint provides the equivalent amount of carbon monoxide as 5 tobacco cigarettes.
- One joint provides the equivalent amount of tar as 3 tobacco cigarettes.

The link between throat and neck cancer is much less argued. Cannabis smoke tends to concentrate in the larger, upper passages of the respiratory tract. Cigarette smoke, on the other hand, is more likely to penetrate the smaller, lower air passageways, where most tobacco-related lung cancers originate. Given that the total tissue area in the upper respiratory passages is much smaller than that in the lower passages, marijuana smokers may well be exposing their throats to a proportionately much greater concentration of carcinogens. It is therefore possible that marijuana is a greater risk to the throat than cigarettes are to the lungs.

This has been confirmed by a study at New York's Memorial Sloan-Kettering Cancer Center showing a 2.1 to 4.9 times greater risk of developing head or neck cancer versus those who had never used the drug (Zhang et al., 1999). The principal author of the study, Zuo-Feng Zhang, stated, "If marijuana smoking has anything to do with smoking-related cancer, the oral cavity would be the first site being affected."

As with cigarettes, developing cancer from smoking marijuana is going to take a considerable amount of time. For those of you that have been smoking for 20 years or more, it may be important to remind yourself—20 years is a lot of time! If you value your own health, and if there are people in your life who also value you staying healthy, this might be extremely motivating for you to quit.

But What About Those Positive Benefits?

Despite all of the research to the contrary, there are people still pushing various so-called benefits of ingesting THC. Without a doubt, marijuana can have beneficial pain-relieving effects, which is why it is being approved for medical use in so many states. As for the other alleged benefits, the research just isn't very solid.

One such benefit being touted is that marijuana has a protective effect against lung cancer. This is partly based on a study that indicated a decrease in tumor size of lab mice that were implanted with human lung cancer cells. This study did show a 50% reduction in the size and weight of the tumors, but there are inherent problems with this line of reasoning.

First, the notion that pot might be able to "prevent" cancer is not a valid excuse to smoke. Yes, I know this finding says nothing about preventing lung cancer, but the majority of those attempting to validate the use of marijuana will distort this study to justify smoking based upon some preventative notion.

Secondly, THC is simply mimicking what your body should be doing naturally. THC targets the cannabinoid receptors and is similar in function to endocannabinoids. Endocannabinoids are cannabinoids, like THC, but are produced naturally by the body. Endocannabinoids, not THC, are intended to activate these receptors.

Finally, the research mice involved with the study were injected with THC. I am unaware of anyone who injects a pure form of synthetic THC. Regarding risk-to-benefit ratios, how can the combustive smoke from this plant, and the resultant host of toxic chemicals and solid particulates infused into the airways of your lungs, be considered beneficial? It is an absurd argument to try to defend.

The Bottom Line is . . .

There is no debate that marijuana damages the health of heavy users, especially those who begin using as teenagers. When examining popular online bookstores for information associated with marijuana, I was shocked to find that the majority of books were directed toward cultivating or preparing the plants for users. Conversely, a search on PubMed's online research site on marijuana provided more than 14,000 studies, the majority of which demonstrated the adverse effects of heavy marijuana use on individuals.

The question you must ask yourself is should you put your trust in the advice of those who continue to do exactly what you are trying to avoid, or should you listen to professional researchers and scientists, who have unbiased data proving the harmful effects of heavy marijuana use? Should we really continue to participate in something that has been proven to unequivocally have risks associated with its frequent and heavy use?

CHAPTER 9

Marijuana and the Brain

The human brain is the last, and greatest,
scientific frontier. It is truly an internal cosmos that
lies contained within our skulls. The more than
100 billion nerve cells and trillion supporting cells
that make up your brain and mine constitute the
most elaborate structure in the known universe.

Joel Davis, *Mapping the Mind*

So much about smoking marijuana ultimately is linked to your brain. From the stimulation of appetite to the addiction itself, we are, in most instances, simply responding to the secretions or lack of secretions of various substances in the brain, when either smoking marijuana or even thinking about it.

To sift through this complex network of brain regions and their interrelated functions is a daunting task. Therefore, I will touch on some of the better-known areas of the brain, and the effect marijuana has on those regions.

The point of this chapter is to help you understand that the brain controls your behavior, cravings, and other emotions with regard to marijuana. This is especially true during the beginning stages of quitting. Your brain will attempt to convince you that you still need the drug. It will crave more stimulation by the chemicals that make you feel good, or happy.

However, it's not your brain's fault. You have simply retrained it by repeatedly supplying it with a synthetic pleasure-inducing substance and altered its function temporarily. But don't be fooled. The emotions you feel are not real and will disappear once the brain starts to respond the way it should.

In a moment, I will write about the effects that marijuana has on the brain. However, before we get started, let's discuss why these areas seem to be so receptive to marijuana in the first place.

We have touched briefly on the receptors that THC attaches to in the body. The most common of these are CB1 and CB2 (Cannabinoid-1, Cannabinoid-2). The CB1 receptor is found in the brain. The CB2 receptor is found outside the brain, in the body, and is of less significance to us when it comes to addiction.

The highest density of CB1 receptors is found in parts of the brain that influence pleasure, memory, thoughts, concentration, time perception, and coordinated movement. Of course, it doesn't take a rocket scientist to figure that out, does it? However, these receptors were not created for the use of THC from marijuana, as some people would like to believe. The body creates its own chemicals called endocannabinoids which are intended for the body to use at these sites.

The brain uses these endocannabinoids in very small amounts, for very short periods of time, and releases them to a particular region for specific reasons. This is quite different from smoking marijuana, which saturates the receptors with exorbitant amounts of THC for very long periods. When this happens, the receptor becomes so resistant that you need more and more of the drug to get the intended response.

Marijuana, Memory, and the Hippocampus

One of the well-established effects of long-term, heavy marijuana use is an impairment of short-term memory. Marijuana's damage to short-term memory seems to occur because THC alters the way in which information is processed by the hippocampus, an area of the brain responsible for memory formation. For example, laboratory rats treated with THC display the same reduced ability to perform tasks requiring short-term memory as other rats showed after nerve cells in their hippocampus were destroyed. I know, you're not a rat, but the human brain functions in very similar ways.

The hippocampus is critical for the formation of new memories. It may function as a memory "gateway" through which new memories must pass before entering permanent storage in the brain. When it doesn't function properly, remembering becomes difficult and learning can be impaired.

Many people claim that marijuana has no impact on their memory. Regarding older memories that have already been stored, this is true. These are stored in a different part of your brain. I don't think anyone has ever forgotten their spouse's name after a marathon smoking session. But short-term and newer memories are definitely affected.

Balance, Coordination and the Cerebellum

A very high density of CB1 receptors is found in a part of the brain known as the cerebellum. Once believed to be exclusively responsible for overall balance, posture, and coordination, scientists now understand this area is also involved in functions other than those associated with movement or motor control. In a study by the Department of Neurology at Boston's Children's Hospital

(Limperopoulos et al., 2005), researchers found that 61 percent of the children with cerebellar injury had global developmental delays, including deficits in language, visual reception and social/behavioral function, in addition to motor control problems.

When I was smoking, its effects on movement alone prevented me from ever wanting to drive under the influence. In fact, it was this impact on the cerebellum that led me to simply remain immobile. I found it too exhausting to put my body in motion, except for the parts that I used to power the X-Box controller. Those were a bit easier to move around than an entire arm or leg!

My Appetite is Out of Control!

Food and marijuana constitute a special problem, because excess food can contribute to diabetes, obesity, and heart disease. For more than 90% of people, marijuana has a significant impact on the brain's appetite control centers. Unfortunately, the preferred foods of smokers are usually not the healthiest of choices. We typically crave higher fat and sweeter foods. Further complicating the situation is our inability to regulate the amount of food we intake. It's a brain thing!

The area of the brain that is the main culprit in increasing appetite is the hypothalamus. The hypothalamus is extremely powerful in that it controls body temperature, hunger, thirst, fatigue, and sleep cycles. As you may know, many of these are affected while you are intoxicated with marijuana. Once again, you are simply replacing the body's natural cannabinoids with THC, by competing for the same receptor sites. The excessive amount of THC is throwing the body's natural regulation out of balance.

Another hormone that is being affected is leptin. Leptin is a hormone that essentially tells the brain when it is time to lose weight. Basically, it shuts down hunger and appetite when it is time to stop eating. The hypothalamus, endocannabinoids, and leptin all work together harmoniously to control food intake. I was always amazed at the amount of food I could shove into my stomach on any given day. There is no doubt that I could have given those hot dog eating champions a run for their money!

Distorted Perceptions and Creativity: It's Just an Illusion

Sensory perception is the realm in which artists are created, where musicians flourish, and well, everyone else just seems to appreciate things more. Many, if not most, marijuana users will swear that smoking enhances their creativity. But the idea that smoking marijuana makes you more creative is a distortion of truth that, essentially, the brain creates for itself.

In truth, by smoking marijuana, you are *not* more creative. You are not funnier. You don't write better or make better music. The enhanced enjoyment of food, movies, and all the other things we enjoy while being stoned are just illusions of enhanced sensory perception created by the brain. Admittedly, it's hard to argue against your own brain. But in this case, you need to. Enhancing the world around you is fun. I understand that. It's just not real.

The weed simply has you appreciating these things on a different level. And that is a major problem. Learning to be sober again so that you can view and appreciate things as they were intended to be is sometimes difficult. However, the longer you are away from smoking, the easier it gets for you to become you.

If you are an artist, writer, or musician, you have the ability to be creative without pot. You would not have been given the talent and passion to do these things if you needed to be "high" in order to perform. Furthermore, drug use has destroyed many more careers than it has enhanced.

The sensory portions of the cerebral cortex are how marijuana enhances our perceptions. Some areas, such as the sensory portion of the cerebral cortex, are responsible for functions related to vision, hearing, touch, movement, and smell. Given THC's ability to enhance the cannabinoids receptors' actions, this gives the user a whole new level of perception related to these functions. Users feel more "in tune" with the world and claim to see brighter colors, hear new sounds, and have an increased level of creativity. But the reality is that to sober people, people high on drugs sound ridiculous.

Pot Makes Me Smarter!

No, it doesn't! This is another lie your brain tells itself. You might think you are smarter, but the distorted perceptions are simply having their way with you again.

When doing research, I found one article titled "Pot Makes Me Smart!" and another titled "Pot Does Rot Your Brain." Both were citing the same study! That study was done by Peter Fried, who tested the IQ scores of marijuana smokers. The actual conclusion of his research was that marijuana does not appear to have a long-term effect on intelligence, but heavy use is detrimental to present cognitive function. Basically, when you stop smoking, things eventually return to the way they were, thankfully. But if you are presently smoking heavily, you are most likely firing on a few less cylinders.

Peter Fried is not the only researcher to obtain these results. Many other studies have shown that performance on a variety of tests of cognitive function is impaired by marijuana. Much of the impairment on cognition points back to the cerebral cortex, but given the interconnectedness of the brain, other regions play their part as well.

Among the impairments of cognitive function that have been observed are a decreased ability to inhibit responses, decreased attention, decreased ability to perform complex mental arithmetic, and impairments to complex reaction times. On the other hand, intoxicated subjects can perform simple arithmetic, learn simple lists of words, and recall memories previously stored. Once again, you have to decide which version of "you" is best suited for the life you want to live.

Some well-designed studies have shown subtle persistent cognitive deficits in individuals who have smoked heavily for longer durations, such as ten years or more. However, these deficits, if they exist, are very small and, more than likely, unnoticeable to you. The most important point to remember is that marijuana does not benefit you intellectually, especially if you continue to smoke on a heavy and frequent basis.

Anxiety and Stress . . . Is It Real?

Whether smoking marijuana reduces anxiety or increases anxiety (or paranoia) depends upon which smoker you listen to. Personally, I believe there is much more evidence favoring a reduction in anxious behaviors due to marijuana's effect on stress hormones within the amygdala, and the enhanced release of dopamine in other parts of the brain. Basically, the reason most people smoke is due to marijuana's ability to help us "chill out."

However, there are two important considerations regarding anxiety: (1) the anxious or stressful feelings that lead us to smoke when we wake up or as soon as we get home, and (2) the feeling of anxiousness that leads us back to smoking when we attempt to quit. In essence, one helps us stay on the path of mediocrity, while the other leads us back when we try to take a different path.

A small pair of organs called the amygdala contribute to these feelings. The amygdala is part of the limbic system. The limbic system is that part of the brain that produces all of the "feel good" hormones, such as dopamine and serotonin. The amygdala's primary role is the processing and memory of emotional reactions, such as anxiety or the "flight-or-fight" response. In other words, the amygdala helps store emotional memories.

It should come as no surprise that parts of the amygdala contain moderate amounts of cannabinoid receptors. Brain scans from one study (Katona, et al., 2001) showed the amygdala had approximately 6-12% less volume in men who smoked heavily (five marijuana cigarettes daily for an average of 20 years) compared to nonusers.

When we stop smoking, these receptors start to "rebalance" or reactivate their normal processes. During this time of rebalancing, however, we can experience a period of possibly intense anxiety or stress, similar to what the hypothalamus might be doing when we experience the horrendous night sweats. We can let this stress lead us back to chronic smoking, or we can understand that the body is going through the process of normalizing now that the receptors are being allowed to breathe again.

If we understand that these feelings of anxiousness are the brain's reaction to the constant insult of an unnatural substance replacing the natural, it should become easier to know that these feelings you experience will pass. You will eventually begin to respond to life as you were truly intended. Allow yourself to go through this process. It will not kill you, no matter how difficult it may seem at the time.

In Conclusion

The brain is a very complex network of neural wires and chemical reactions so interconnected that our understanding, in terms of addiction, is limited. As Ruth and Gerald Fischbach noted,

> When we deal with brain science, we are dealing with the organ that makes us unique individuals, that gives us our personality, memories, emotions, dreams, creative abilities, and at times our sinister selves.

Nevertheless, we do understand that the brain is a major contributor in helping guide you back to the same destructive patterns, time after time. As I have said, marijuana intoxication can cause distorted perceptions, impaired coordination, difficulty in thinking and problem solving, and problems with learning and memory. These effects are not long-term, lasting only a few weeks according to most research. However, heavy use substantially impairs performance, both mentally and physically.

The bottom line is that your brain changes significantly while you are high. It is never a good thing to alter your body's natural bio- or neurochemistry. It may be pleasurable for short periods, but to continually bombard it with artificial stimulation is harmful. When you change your brain chemistry, you change. What purpose does this change have for you? Is it beneficial to you, or to the people around you?

The very good news is that, after you stop smoking, your brain will pretty quickly start to adapt to what it wants to do, which is to function normally, producing feel-good hormones on its own, and not have its neurons constantly bombarded with artificial external stimulation. Your body will breathe a big sigh of relief, both literally and figuratively: "Whew! This feels much better. Thank you for letting me function like I was designed to!" In other words, your own body will itself help you in this process. But you have to choose to let it.

CHAPTER 10

The Dopamine Reward System

I used to think things were more enjoyable while smoking. But, in reality, most things were less enjoyable because I was only half there and fighting to pay attention. I used to use weed to energize and motivate me, and it did that sometimes, but it also tired me out and zapped my motivation.

Anonymous

You really can't have a discussion about addiction without discussing the impact that most drugs have on increasing dopamine levels. This alteration in dopamine is what is basically making us feel better. And the ultimate goal of any compulsive disorder is to try to make us feel better, right?

This chapter could easily be considered as part of the last chapter, of course, since dopamine is produced by the brain. But the role of dopamine is so vital in regard to marijuana addiction that I felt is deserved its own chapter.

What is dopamine? Dopamine is a very important neurotransmitter in the brain, with many different functions. Most importantly, it is central to the brain's reward system. Dopamine is commonly associated with the pleasure system of the brain, providing feelings of enjoyment and reinforcement which motivate a person to perform certain activities. This neurotransmitter is released by naturally rewarding experiences such as food and sex, the use of certain drugs, and other pleasurable stimuli. Basically, the pleasant feelings associated with the dopamine response keep you coming back for more.

Marijuana, or THC specifically, creates changes in the dopamine system similar to other drugs such as cocaine, amphetamines, nicotine, and alcohol. Their actions on the brain differ slightly, but an overall increase in dopamine is the end result. Marijuana has been known, however, to directly enhance the release of dopamine in certain brain regions rather than to prevent the uptake of what dopamine is already there.

This direct stimulation implies that the body's own cannabinoid system is somehow involved in regulating dopamine release. By smoking on a regular basis, we begin to tamper with the natural processes of the body by interfering with the finely tuned releases of dopamine in our brain. This entire process is complicated and involves more than just one neurotransmitter.

We seek to stimulate more dopamine release for a variety of reasons. From a recreational standpoint, it's just fun. Obviously, this is why recreational drug use, including alcohol, has been around for centuries and remains so prevalent in the world today. I am not, in any way, promoting illegal drug use, but simply pointing out the "why." Stress is another mitigating factor for many individuals who smoke marijuana on a daily basis.

The ultimate goal at this time, however, is get back to a point in which we are able to allow the body to produce dopamine without the need of an external source. So, let's first discuss what this constant artificial stimulation of dopamine does to the system.

I am continually returning to the body's unique ability to stay in balance. The proper term for this balance is homeostasis.

It is mind-boggling how the human body sustains this balancing act with millions upon millions of processes that operate simultaneously. The proper amounts of dopamine secreted are no exception.

We know that for any chemical to be processed in the body, like a neurotransmitter, there has to be a receptor waiting on the other side to receive it. In order for the body to maintain the proper balance of dopamine after overstimulation, the body will actually decrease the number of receptors. The remaining receptors will also become less sensitive to dopamine. This process is called desensitization.

Desensitization is better known as tolerance, where exposure to a drug causes less of a response than previously obtained. As a result, when we are not using marijuana, we are left with a situation in which our dopamine levels are limited, due to the constant artificial stimulation of this neurotransmitter. Combine this with the condition of having fewer receptors to process what little dopamine is left, and we get an individual who is on the verge of a nervous breakdown.

Kenneth Blum, Ph.D., one of the top researchers in the world on addiction and the dopamine system, has coined the term "brain reward cascade" to describe the complex interaction of neurotransmitters in the reward system of the brain. In fact, Dr. Blum has discovered and researched a condition known as "Reward Deficiency Syndrome" (RDS) showing that addiction-prone individuals may possess a genetic anomaly altering the way they are able to process dopamine.

Dr. Blum has identified a gene that apparently has been altered in individuals prone to addictive or compulsive behaviors. Furthermore, RDS can be manifested in relatively mild or severe forms which are related to an individual's biochemical inability to derive reward from ordinary, everyday activities. The research behind this concept is actually pretty solid.

In individuals possessing an abnormality with a specific dopamine receptor gene, we think the brain lacks sufficient numbers of dopamine receptor sites. In essence, without a sufficient number of receptors to utilize dopamine, the brain will reduce the amount of dopamine produced. Impairment of the brain reward cascade ultimately leads to a reduction of net dopamine release, a reduction in dopamine receptors, and the resultant enhancement of substance craving activity.

What if the problem is not just the "love" of smoking marijuana, but a more specific problem related to a genetic condition, like RDS? Is there a pattern in your life where you have tendencies to engage in activities, specifically those that are considered risky or destructive, simply to increase brain dopamine function?

So is addiction a "gene" thing? Unfortunately, we often love to blame our circumstances or conditions on genes. In my practice, I have heard people fault their genetic make-up as to why they are overweight, depressed, have diabetes or hypertension, or even lower back problems. They never once mention how they eat, move, or think. It definitely sounds better to say you have a genetic problem than to admit it is just a lack of control or willpower.

Undoubtedly, our genes are responsible in many ways for how we function. But the point I am trying to make is that genes, for the most part, are like a light switch. Someone, or something, has to flip the switch to turn it on. For example, you might have the genetic predisposition for diabetes, but the sugar responsible for the condition had to be placed in your mouth first.

We could accurately say that by first engaging in potentially addictive behaviors, we are opening Pandora's Box. Yes, the gene for "addiction," so to speak, might be triggering the irrational reward seeking behaviors. But the choice is yours as to whether to keep the box open. No one's genes force them to engage in ongoing behaviors. To close the box, you have to be proactive and quit "flipping the switch" that keeps the addiction going.

In summary, whether it is a genetic anomaly, long-term continuing stress, or long-term abuse of substances that is responsible for the addictive behavior, dopamine will need to be restored naturally after quitting marijuana. So, we have two choices. We can wait, feeling anxious and depressed, until our system attempts to normalize dopamine production amongst other neurotransmitters, or we can be proactive and start helping our body produce the necessary dopamine on its own.

One way to do that is by regularly engaging in healthier activities (also called *habits*!) that will enhance such dopamine production. Exercise is one of those activities. So is getting more sun. So is getting enough sleep. So is sex. Am I saying that it may be good to have more sex? Yes! Who says that kicking your marijuana habit has to be all work and no play?

In addition—and this is key—I very strongly suggest utilizing the amino acid supplements suggested in Chapter 20. Amino acids are precursors to the production of neurotransmitters, like dopamine and serotonin. Therefore, they are the essential ingredients needed to produce these substances. As we will discuss, most of the amino acids can be found in the foods we eat, but not in the quantities we will need initially to help "tweak" the system, as it is restored to normal.

PART III

A NEW WAY OF LIFE

CHAPTER 11

Getting Started

I'm tired of not living up to my potential. I want to
do so much more with my existence than smoking
weed all day imagining weird situations and playing
out scenes in my life that will never happen.
Anonymous

In many ways, the motivation you have right now to quit marijuana is such an exciting and refreshing emotion. Finally, after all the years of cycling through the motions of "to quit or not to quit," and the guilt or weakness experienced when you fail, there comes a time when you truly become dedicated to this promise.

Day One is filled with mixed emotions and each person has varying degrees of confidence and reasons to quit, just as there are many reasons why you smoke. Although the motivation or reason to quit is the cornerstone, you really need to have a structured plan, not only to deal with the physical withdrawals, but the mental withdrawals as well. To simply deal with the emotions you experience is very difficult.

This is one of the reasons why so many people fail the first few (or many!) times. I am sure you would not be surprised to know that more people fail than succeed. I know this may sound pessimistic, but it is the reality of this addiction. In fact, more people fail at abstaining from smoking marijuana than all other illegal drugs combined.

Quitting takes a tremendous amount of proactive work. If someone expects to sit idly and wait for these symptoms and emotions to simply disappear, then failure is imminent in most cases.

For some of you, this is a very difficult situation. To some, it might seem as if there is no hope in your life personally and professionally. Your world may even seem to be crashing down around you, but you do not have to crash with it. You need to get a hold of yourself *now* and wake up to the true reality around you. Some of you are looking at this as if you are victim, and feeling helpless as a result. You have, in many ways, been the main participant in creating this life you are now living. Shouldn't you have the power to un-create it as well?

It is not going to be easy, which I am sure you already know. It is funny how the weed becomes our escape, and yet it is simultaneously complicating the very problems that exist. It is difficult enough in life to deal with our weaknesses, much less have them compounded by something that dulls our ability to confront them appropriately, and ruins our own natural ability to cope.

The problems that existed before the smoking do not magically disappear. Becoming cognizant of these problems is a good place to start understanding why you have become a chronic smoker.

There might be things you have done that you are not particularly proud of, but these actions are not truly you. Most of you can remember what you were like before you started the smoking. Sadly, many of you do not really believe you can become that person again. But you can. In fact, you are still that person; you just need to start being that person.

I know this is going to sound like strange advice, but if you are having a difficult time, do not stop smoking for the next few days. You need to get your head straight and prepare yourself before going through what you are about to experience. What you need more than anything right now is hope that there is a solution for you . . . and there is, I promise.

If you haven't already done so, you need to decide upon a quit day. If you have already quit, continue on with your plan. But for those that haven't, my advice is to select your quit day at the beginning of the weekend. That's right. The beginning of the week, such as Monday, is typically the day that is chosen to break any bad habit and start anew. This doesn't just apply to smoking.

The problem is this: if we start on Monday, by the time the weekend comes around we seem to be a little weaker from the stresses of the week, and the weekends, being a huge "trigger," can lead to failure. On the other hand, if you start off on a weekend and actually make it through the weekend, when your resolve and emotion to quit are still strong, you are off to a good start.

Throughout the book, we will discuss strategies for you to begin this journey. Although much emphasis is on the various methods we can use, the change in our beliefs and our motivations to quit are, by far, the most important. Combine that change in beliefs and motivation with a workable plan, and you're ready. As the novelist Saul Bellow said, "A plan relieves you of the torment of choice." Besides, having a plan to abstain is far better than the maverick "cold turkey" approach to quitting.

I want to share an excerpt from Robin Sharma's book *The Greatness Guide* entitled "On Mountains of Mastering Change" where he uses the metaphor of mountain climbing to illustrate that "people truly can make changes that last."

Define What the Mountaintop Looks Like

I suggest you articulate, in writing, what success looks like. Note what needs to change in your life for you to feel spectacularly successful and what will happen if you don't improve. Then record your goals in all the key areas of your life. Write out what you want your reality to appear as five years from now. List the values you want to stand for. Clarity precedes success—and awareness precedes transformation.

Start Climbing

There's great power in starting (I call it the Power of Start). A single act—done now—sets the forces into play. It generates momentum. And with the action you begin to experience positive results. That begins a positive feedback loop: more action, more results. And that, in turn, promotes confidence.

Take Small Steps

You can't get to the top of Everest by jumping up the mountain. You get to the mountaintop by taking incremental steps. Step by step you get to the goal. Every step gets you closer to the dream. Life's like that too. Small steps each day get you to greatness over time. Why? Because the days really do become weeks and weeks become months and months become years. You'll get to the end of your life anyway—why not reach that place as an extraordinary human being?

Thanks Robin. You may never know how much that metaphor actually helps.

Any huge commitment we make in life should bear some type of contract. Don't you agree? You would also agree that this is a HUGE commitment.

So then, let's start by signing your very own CAARE (Cannabis Addiction and Recovery Empowerment) Contract. Let's make this official and not just some emotional whim you have decided to embark upon. If you are not ready to sign it right now, then wait until tomorrow. Think about it overnight if you have to. Is this really something you are ready to do? Are you willing to go through the difficult times during the next few weeks?

If so, sign the CAARE Contract on the next page.

✏ PERSONAL TASK #5
My Commitment to Stop Using Contract

I hereby commit to, and accept responsibility for, achieving the goals that I have initialed below. These goals are designed to prepare me to stop getting high. In addition, they show my motivation, confidence, and commitment to the quitting process. I understand that a slip can occur and I must not use it as an excuse to return to use.

1. I will follow the helpful hints and keep in mind what I am experiencing is normal.

2. I will begin to increase my physical activities. I commit to:

   _____

   _____

3. I will throw away all of my paraphernalia. (No holding on to anything for old time's sake).

4. I will avoid places where there are temptations to get high, such as bars and time with friends who get high.

5. I will drink an extra two glasses of water each day.

6. I will reward myself for accomplishing these goals by:

   _____

   _____

MY QUIT DATE IS: _____

Signature _____

Today's date _____

CHAPTER 12

Your Relapse Prevention Plan

I like the movie *The Hunt for Red October*, a Cold War story about a Russian nuclear submarine captain (played by Sean Connery) who, along with his senior officers, decides to sail to the U.S. and defect. It's a dangerous gambit; the whole Russians navy is trying to sink the sub, and the U.S. navy will soon start trying as well. A CIA agent (Alec Baldwin) flies to a U.S. aircraft carrier in the Atlantic to try to establish communication with the sub. The carrier commander challenges the much younger Baldwin with this question (my apologies to all my Russian friends!):

> "What his plan? Russians don't take a dump, son, without a plan. Senior captains don't start something this dangerous without having thought the matter through."

That's *exactly* the perspective you have to have at this point. If you are going to start something this life-changing, you are going to have to *seriously* think this thing through. I don't mean seriously think through whether you want to make such a positive change in your life. Let's assume at this point that you've made that decision. I mean seriously think through *how* you are going to do it. How is that submarine captain going to avoid getting sunk by his own navy, and also by the American navy? How are you going to avoid getting sunk by all of the things arrayed against you—and they are numerous. You certainly *can* do it. But you need to have a plan.

That's what this section is for: helping you create a specific, step-by-step plan. You could accurately call this your Relapse Prevention Plan. If you think about it, deciding to quit smoking is not the hard part. And starting to quit smoking is not the hard part. Go for the next four hours without smoking. You've started to quit! Anyone can do that. *Staying* quit is the hard part. As Mark Twain reportedly said about tobacco, "To cease smoking is the easiest thing I ever did. I ought to know because I've done it a thousand times."

Here are a couple of statistics that should serve as a warning that this journey you are about to go on *will not be easy.*

- On average, adults with an average daily marijuana use of more than a decade have entered treatment programs *six or more times.*
- Treatment outcomes for adolescent and young adult marijuana users show post-treatment abstinence rates of *less than 15 percent.*

You can definitely do this. I know that from personal experience. But you have to think it through. Having a written, easily accessible plan in advance is essential to help you stay committed to your goal when a potential relapse is looming in the shadows. A relapse prevention plan that is written down can serve as a blueprint to fall back on in times of stress, reminding you of your options in the moment and of your goals for moving forward. It can keep you accountable and focused on recovery.

I want to highlight two things about a relapse prevention plan. First, it is highly personal. It is tailored to your own specific circumstances, personality, triggers, and needs. Cookie-cutter, one-size-fits-all plans are probably better than nothing, but they aren't nearly as good as a plan that you yourself have created to suit your own unique needs.

And second, it is detailed. The more specific your plan is, the more likely it is to be helpful in a wide variety of situations and events that you will inevitably encounter. It doesn't help much to say to someone, "When you are tempted to smoke, just distract yourself with something else." *OK, fine*, you will say. *How?* You need to have that figured out before you get into the situation. Otherwise, you're just winging it, and winging it isn't going to cut it—not if you're serious about learning a new, healthy way to live.

So your plan does need to be specific, but it is not *unchangeable*. Just the opposite, in fact—you will need to adapt it over time as you progress and your needs at any point in time begin to change. That could well happen within a couple of weeks.

So, let's get started. First, we are going to think through some important issues and have some plans in place before you quit, so they will be immediately ready for you to implement as part of your plan. And, if you have already quit, fantastic! You're ahead of the curve. Let's get these things into place immediately for you to have as tools.

On the following pages, you will create your own personal plan. It will consist of eleven steps that focus on things like personal goals that are important to you, identifying triggers and what to do when they surface, maintaining a healthy lifestyle, and managing relationships and support systems.

Is this going to take a bit of time and thought to develop? Yes. Is it a drop in the ocean compared to the time you have spent on your habit? Yes. So let's get real. Your life, and the lives of those around you, are worth every minute that you commit to this process. Please take this plan seriously enough to spend the appropriate time to not only complete it but to complete it thoroughly. I promise you that it will come in handy at some point.

Planning Step 1: Identify your personal goals in recovery and motivations for positive changes.

It is important for you to think about what you want out of recovery and what your own personal goals for the future are. What changes are you willing to make, and what are your motivations for making them? For instance, things like keeping a job, making amends and improving relationships with loved ones, consistently fulfilling family obligations, becoming physically healthier, or enhancing self-esteem can all be great goals to strive for in recovery and things to include in your plan.

Please spend some time to really think about what it is that you are wanting to accomplish by removing this habit from your life. (You did some of this work in Personal Task #3 on page 25.) Here are a few more examples of what this may look like.

PERSONAL GOALS FOR SELF-IMPROVEMENT:

- I want to be more physically fit and live a healthier lifestyle.
- I want to regain/maintain my position at my job and develop more financial stability.
- I want to learn to control my anger by staying calm and controlling my emotions in a much healthier way.
- I want to make amends with friends and family members who have suffered as a result of my addiction and seek to improve these relationships.
- I want to stop feeling enslaved to any addiction or habit and live with a sense of personal freedom and power that comes with that freedom.
- I want to have adequate time and emotional availability for those I am close to.

Having considered your own personal goals, write the most important ones down here:

1. _____
2. _____
3. _____
4. _____
5. _____

Planning Step 2: Identity triggers (people, places, routines, times of day) for your own marijuana use.

We are going to discuss triggers and relapses in more detail later, but before we get to that particular section of the book, you will need to have a plan in advance in order to avoid and/or deal with them.

A trigger is something that can induce cravings to light up. Each person will have their own specific triggers. They may be caused by certain events, places, people, or circumstances. For instance, you may frequent certain places where you always smoked with your buddies, and these people and/or places may need to be avoided, at least for a while. Triggers and cravings are a part of the process, and it is important to have coping mechanisms and tools in place for managing them in a healthy manner.

What specific things will be the biggest challenges for you personally? Although our list of triggers can be very long, **please list 5 potential triggers or challenges** you may face that could cause you to start using again. If you can't come up with five, you aren't looking hard enough. Most people have three to four times that amount.

Here are some examples:

- I get triggered by the pot and smoking paraphernalia I have at my house (OK, this one is kind of a no-brainer)
- Every day when I come home from work, I turn on the TV and light up (this is a routine)

- Every time I go over to Joe's, we light up (this is a person who is a trigger)
- I go to parties or get-togethers where I light up (these are people and events that are triggers)
- I light up every time I start to feel stressed in my significant relationships, job-related stress, or financial stress

Simply avoiding (or escaping from) people, places, and situations that make you want to smoke is often this is the easiest and most effective way to avoid and resist temptation—certainly in the beginning. And it's just common sense. You can't expect yourself to break the pot habit if you are constantly putting yourself in these situations. It just won't work. You're deceiving yourself if you think it will. Will this mean changing who you hang out with? Yes, probably. Will it hurt their feelings? Maybe so. But if they cannot support you in this, how valuable is their friendship, really?

OK, think about your own personal triggers and list at least five that you believe are the most important. Be *especially* honest with yourself as to which people serve as triggers for you.

1. _____
2. _____
3. _____
4. _____
5. _____

Planning Step 3: Make a plan to change any smoking-related routines

All right, now we are going to get concrete about making plans to change, or counter, specific triggers. That's what the next several steps are going to be about. We will take them one at a time. First: routines. What routines did you list that regularly contribute to your smoking habit? You need to make a plan to change those routines.

This doesn't mean that the routine needs to be abandoned forever, but it does need to be changed for now if it is triggering you.

For example, we mentioned coming home from work, sitting down in the living room, turning on the TV, and lighting up. For you, that may be a routine. You do it almost every day. You can count on it. That's a huge trigger. The minute you walk through the front door and head for the living room, you're already in the smoking cycle. Your brain knows exactly what comes next. It is chemically pushing you *toward* what comes next. So you have to change that routine.

"But I like watching TV when I get home from work!" you say. Look, I'm not suggesting that you never watch TV again for the rest of your life. I'm just saying change your routine *for now*. Will that be uncomfortable? Almost certainly. That's the whole point. You've been way too comfortable way too long in this unhealthy lifestyle. You're adopting a new way of living.

Instead of doing that every day when you come home from work, for instance, you might immediately take the dog for a walk. You might go jogging, or go for a walk, and then take a shower when you get back. You might play a video game with your kid. If you like to cook, you might go straight to the kitchen, make a healthy snack, and maybe even start dinner. There are a lot of things you *could* do instead of your routine. People all around *do* do other things when they get home from work other than your routine. You just need to establish a new routine for yourself.

So, what are your primary smoking routines, and what are some *realistic* replacement routines that you could adopt instead?

My current routine: _____

_____

_____

_____

One or two realistic alternative routines: _____

_____

_____

_____

My current routine: _____

_____

_____

_____

One or two realistic alternative routines: _____

_____

_____

_____

Planning Step 4: Make a plan to engage relationships that support your new lifestyle.

Relationships are key to your new lifestyle. They can either contribute mightily toward your success or toward your failure. The people around you can be great resources to help you through this process, or they can just as easily, in a matter of seconds, destroy every effort you make to get through this. As a result, you *must* surround yourself with people who support your goals and can contribute toward helping you achieve these goals.

Really, this is true in all of life, not just in kicking the marijuana habit. Some people lift you up and help propel you toward being all you were designed to be. Some people drag you down and help you languish in mediocrity, or worse. At this point, you need to actively choose the former and activity avoid the latter.

In Step 2, you should have already identified people who serve as triggers in your life. These are people you will have to avoid, or if that simply isn't possible, people you need to at least relate to in a safer environment (such as at a ballgame or a restaurant, not at cousin Joe's smoke-filled apartment!).

At this point, there are two other groups of people you need to identify. One group of people are the ones you want to associate with to stay on the right path. These are the people who have a positive influence on your life, or who could have a positive influence on your life if you gave them the chance. They can genuinely motivate you to be a better version of yourself. You have people like this in your life. Everyone does. If you don't know them well, now's your chance to get to know them well and see how enjoyable they can be. You need them.

List 5 people (with phone numbers) you should associate with to stay on a healthy path away from marijuana use.

1. _____ (number)
2. _____ (number)
3. _____ (number)
4. _____ (number)
5. _____ (number)

I find that it's helpful for you to give some thought to activities you may be able to engage in with these people. Maybe you only know them at work. Now's your chance to get to know them outside of work. Next to each of the people you listed above, jot down one or two things you could do with them to spend time with them, get to know them better, or just enjoy your current friendship with them. Go to a restaurant or a coffee shop. Go shopping. Go to a movie or a ballgame. Go play Frisbee golf. Go to a bookstore. Go for a walk together. Be creative!

The second group of people you will need to identify are the ones you can contact in case you feel a potential relapse coming on. This group and the one above (that you just completed) can overlap, of course. But you may well have people on this list as well that you wouldn't normally socialize with.

It is extremely helpful to have people you can talk to when you need to. Think about ways to communicate effectively and ask for help when you need it. Keep numbers for counselors, mentors, friends, and family nearby, and don't hesitate to talk things out with them. Remember, people like helping people. It makes them feel good and needed. You're not being a burden to people. This is what relationships are for, to help each other grow.

List 5 people (with phone numbers) you can contact if you feel that you are going to relapse.

1. _____ (number)

2. _____ (number)

3. _____ (number)

4. _____ (number)

5. _____ (number)

Planning Step 5: Make a plan to counter triggers by actively engaging your mind.

People who quit pot learn to find activities that engage their mind, so they're not just sitting there being tempted. Do a crossword puzzle. Play "Words with Friends" on your phone. Read an engrossing article or blog. Have a novel handy. Have a nonfiction book handy on a topic you find really interesting. Count backwards from 150 by threes. (OK, that one is not exactly enjoyable, but it is a distraction.) Look up a healthy snack recipe and prepare it.

One great way to engage your mind is to do something for someone else. Get your focus off of yourself. Email a friend and tell them what you appreciate about them. They will be so surprised! Hop in the car, go buy a postcard (they still sell those) and write it and mail it to an old friend or relative. The possibilities are endless.

List here three things that you personally can see yourself doing to engage your mind:

1. _____

2. _____

3. _____

Planning Step 6: Make a plan to counter triggers by actively engaging your body.

When the temptation comes to give in and just have "one more smoke"—and it will come—you need to be proactive in responding to it. Just sitting there mulling over the temptation is *not* the way to handle it. Almost universally, people who quit learn right away to engage their bodies in simply doing something different. Stand up and stretch. I mean really stretch. Do an exercise routine. Go outside. Take a brisk walk. Hop on a bike. Climb a set of stairs. You'll figure out what works best for you.

List here three things that you personally can see yourself doing to engage your body. These may be different depending on the setting you are in (at work or at home, for instance):

1. _____

2. _____

3. _____

Actively engaging your body in the moment is a subset, really, of developing a healthier lifestyle overall, which we will address in a moment.

Planning Step 7: Make a plan to counter triggers by diffusing stress.

Dealing with stress is, for many of us, a major reason why we turn to marijuana. For me, it was probably the major reason. In the long run, it's a really lousy way to deal with stress, because it does nothing to address the issues that are stressing us. In fact, it almost always makes them worse. Nevertheless, it's how we've learned to handle stress.

We need to learn new ways.

Like everything else in this plan, how you best learn to handle stress will be very individualized. One person may learn to love meditating. Another person may run five kilometers a day. You will have to find a method or methods that work for you. Here are some primary ways people learn to handle stress.

Get physical. I mention this here again because it's such an effective stress handler. Regular exercise is a fantastic way to both work off stress and provide your body with feel-good endorphins.

Imagery and visualization. Visualize yourself as a nonsmoker— happy, healthy, and in control; imagine your lungs getting pink and healthy; visualize yourself in healthy relationships, enjoying the people you care about.

(You may also try the opposite: focus on negative imagery and imagine yourself with cancer, emphysema, unable to breathe, and needing constant care; visualize yourself in a jail made of marijuana cigarettes symbolizing the way the drug controls your life. Negative visualization, of course, is not a stress reliver, but I mention it here as a potentially effective way to reinforce your commitment to stop a very destructive habit.)

I discuss visualization more in Chapter 21.

Practice relaxation or meditation techniques regularly. There is some overlap here with imagery and visualization. I discuss meditation more in Chapter 21. I also recommend some resources on the website, secretaddiction.org. I strongly recommend that you learn relaxation techniques, or meditation techniques, or both, that work day in and day out for you. It is a powerful route to a more peaceful, fulfilling life, and a powerful antidote to the stress so many smokers are seeking to escape from.

Develop your spiritual life. Pray regularly. Supplement it with scripture reading. If you are someone who would find this meaningful, I provide some suggested resources at secretaddiction.org.

Deal straight on with social pressure. Be aware when others are smoking. Remember your commitment not to smoke marijuana. Be assertive and request that people not offer you pot. If appropriate, ask that they not smoke around you for a while. If necessary, be prepared to walk away, especially when you've recently quit.

Handle anger, frustration, and interpersonal conflict. Try to handle these situations directly, rather than hiding your feelings, but do so with "I" statements, not "you" statements; the objective is to bring healing to a situation, not more conflict. When appropriate, be assertive. Don't try to escape these situations by engaging in self-destructive behavior. When necessary, get some release from anger by squeezing a rubber ball, pounding a pillow, or doing some physical activity; write down your feelings or tell them to someone; take deep breaths. (I say more about anger management in Chapter 15).

List here two things that you believe would be the best strategies for you to deal with stress on an ongoing basis, and for each write down the first step you need to take toward accomplishing those things.

1. _____

2. _____

Planning Step 8: Make a plan to counter triggers by having fun.
A major part of your success will be learning to engage in activities that replace the role of smoking in your life *and provide you with*

some of the same benefits. Let's face it, most of us smoke because it's fun (at least, it was for quite a while) and we like the way it makes us feel. Simply put, we need to replace our smoking with some activities that we also enjoy, or that we can learn to enjoy. Does this mean that playing Frisbee golf will enable us to bypass withdrawals? No, but engaging in other activities you enjoy will certainly help, and they are vital to you establishing a new, much more positive way of life. And, honestly, who doesn't like to do things they enjoy? You've just let these things be crowded out over time by your smoking.

The bottom line is that people who are content with life involve themselves regularly in things they enjoy doing. You may have had such a thing in the past, or you may need to find such a thing. It develops into something you look forward to doing. For some people it's gardening. For others, it's cooking, or woodworking, or crocheting. Writing and publishing a book (publishing your own book is easy to do now on Amazon, for free!). Blogging. Again, the possibilities are endless. Throw yourself into something and see if it catches your fancy.

Engage in an enjoyable activity several times a week that is not work related. Go play Frisbee golf. Throw a football. Go shopping. Get a manicure or pedicure. Invite non-smoking friends over for a barbeque, or a ballgame. Go see a movie. Have some healthy fun! Non-smoking people do that kind of thing, you know!

One avenue for this is often overlooked but for many people proves to be their primary outlet: volunteering. Don't tell me you don't have time. *Of course* you have time. Do I need to explain why that is obvious? Volunteering not only gets you outside of yourself, it can also provide a deep sense of meaning, connection, and enjoyment. Don't know what the volunteer opportunities are in your area? Do a search on "volunteer opportunities" and "[your city]." I'm guessing whatever comes up could keep you occupied for years.

Make a list of five things you could regularly enjoy doing, or would commit to investigating thoroughly for this purpose (such as volunteering):

1. _____

2. _____

3. _____

4. _____

5. _____

Planning Step 9: Decide beforehand what to do about alcohol.
If you drink alcohol, there are two dangers it presents to your success in quitting marijuana. First, your brain may associate drinking with smoking pot. Either you are used to doing both in one sitting—at home, at parties, wherever—or drinking alcohol may normally lead to you smoking later that evening. Either way, it's problematic. Second, alcohol can make you less vigilant about resisting marijuana. That's pretty obvious. Alcohol simply tends to make people less concerned about long-term consequences. The first few weeks after quitting, you may need to consider not drinking, or at least cutting back on your alcohol consumption. If you don't want to do this, be especially careful when, where, and with whom you drink. You know your own weaknesses best.

Write down here what your plan is concerning alcohol for the next 6-8 weeks:

_____

_____

_____

_____

_____

_____

Planning Step 10: Find ways to develop and maintain a healthy lifestyle.

If you've been a regular pot smoker, chances are good that you need to adopt a heathier lifestyle. Actually, if you simply live in America, chances are good! Quitting pot is not just a convenient time to do this, it's a vital time to do this.

Why? Because to be successful at changing your lifestyle, you are going to need all the support your body and your mind can give you. By adopting a healthier lifestyle, you are getting your body and your mind fully on board. And, in addition, you are taking time that has been devoted to unhealthy living and devoting it instead to healthy living. I've never met anyone who, having adopted a healthier lifestyle, said to me, "You know, I'm really sorry I chose to do that!" You will be *very* glad for the proactive choices you make in this direction.

For the person quitting marijuana, getting healthier has the added benefit of keeping you busy, because it takes time to exercise, to eat right, etc. You can't underestimate the importance of this. As I said earlier, uncommitted time is not your friend, especially in the early stages of quitting.

It can be very beneficial to set up a daily ritual for maintaining physical health, such as a structured sleep schedule, a plan for balanced meals, and a fitness regime. Getting enough sleep and eating healthily can aid in setting up a strong foundation to build upon. Being physically active can help you to have a clearer mind and feel less stressed as well as increase self-confidence.

I address a healthy lifestyle in Chapter 20, and you are welcome to turn there and look at the ideas presented. What's most important in regard to this, however, is that you are consistently moving your life in the right direction. We are all great at making grandiose resolutions. "I'm not going to eat any junk carbs for the rest of my life! Except maybe on Super Bowl Sunday." Right. What are the chances of living up to that?

It's fine to start small, establish a consistent routine, and build from there. You want to join a gym and start working out an hour a day? Great. Go for it. But if the object is simply to start moving, every day, in the right direction, it might do you just as much good to commit to taking a 15 minute walk every day. Remember, you are building a new way of life. Walk. Ride a bike. Play an active sport. Take the stairs instead of the elevator. Park farther away from work and walk the extra distance. Listen to music you love on the way, or motivational talks. On the nutrition side, commit to have a salad each day. Even a vegetable wouldn't hurt! Be creative. But make sure it's something you can start doing, and keep doing. That's the key.

Identify three things you can start regularly doing to move toward a healthier lifestyle. Examples may be as simple as this:

- I will go to bed at the same time every night and plan to get at least seven and a half hours of sleep.
- I will walk at least 15 minutes a day.
- I will eat at least one healthy, balanced meal a day (hey, it's a start!).
- I will make sure I am drinking enough water every day.
- I will start using the gym membership I already have and go exercise three times a week.

Now, make you own list to start. You can adjust this as the days pass, of course.

1. _____
2. _____
3. _____
4. _____
5. _____

Planning Step 11: Devise strategies to keep yourself accountable to the plan.

This final planning step is important, and it is *really* going to have to be individualized. It lends itself to a chart, but I'm not even going to put one in here for you to complete, because the layout itself will look different for different people. If you feel like a chart would help you personally (and I do think it's a very good idea) pull out a sheet of a paper, or an Excel sheet, and make one.

What we're asking in this planning step is basically this: what are some things that for you, personally, will help keep you on track with all of this? For some of you, this may be an **accountability partner**. You need someone to be accountable to every day, kind of like an AA sponsor. If so, great. I strongly advocate having an accountability partner. If this is something you think would help you quite a bit, write this person's name down here:

---

and then contact them and talk it over with them if you have not done so already. Work out between the two of you how this accountability thing is going to work. How often will you check in? Will you meet at times in person? How will you handle any relapses? If you relapse once, will both of you commit to moving forward?

Here's another accountability aid that works for a lot of people: a **personal reward system**. To set one up, you simply make a chart and put on it (1) small, attainable goals, (2) some type of calendar marking off days, so you know when you have met those goals, and (3) specific rewards you give yourself for making positive progress. For instance, you may look at the Financial Cost Calculator you completed and figure out how much your smoking habit has been costing on average every week. At the end of each week of abstinence, you give yourself permission to spend that amount on something you want, or to set aside in a savings account for something you want—a new TV, a backyard deck, whatever. Or maybe there's something for which you'd love to save up for your children. Now's your chance.

What goes on a chart like this, and even the structure of the chart, is going to be up to you. But I do recommend developing a personal reward system. You need to make sure it is something that will help keep *you* motivated.

One more strategy I recommend—and this could go in various places of the book, but I will put it here—is writing out a **gratitude list**. Developing an attitude of gratitude is an incredibly helpful life skill. It makes us thankful for all the good things in our lives (while not dismissing the difficult things) and gives us a healthy sense of humility. It's so easy to focus on the negative, which accomplishes nothing for us. Focusing on the positive instead is incredibly powerful. We can complain that we are stuck in traffic behind someone who isn't taking a right on that red light, or we can be grateful that we own a car (most people in the world don't), that we have the physical health to use it (many people don't), and that we live in a place where traffic flows pretty smoothly because of traffic lights (as a contrast, ever been to Cairo, Egypt?).

The great thing about a gratitude list is that you can add to it endlessly. Here are a few to start. Every one won't apply to you, of course, but many will. I encourage you to add some more now, keep adding some, and come back to this list to read it—out loud is best—regularly.

MY GRATITUDE LIST

- I am thankful for my spouse / partner / family / kids
- I am thankful for my job / source of income
- I am thankful for my sight, my hearing, my senses of touch and smell and taste
- I am thankful for the place where I live

- I am thankful for being able to get around
- I am thankful to live in the country where I live, with so many freedoms and blessings that are easy to take for granted
- I am thankful to have enough to eat
- I am thankful for all the conveniences I own
- I am thankful for being able to access more and better sources of entertainment than anyone in history
- I am thankful for those who care about me
- I am thankful for good friendships
- I am thankful that I can hope, and dream, and have aspirations that I am able to work toward
- I am thankful that I have people who are supporting me right now

- _____
- _____
- _____
- _____
- _____
- _____

SUMMARY

OK, you've done some really good work here. You've identified what your primary goals are in life (and that you need to stop smoking to accomplish). You've identified your primary triggers and smoking routines. You've listed people who can vitally help you in the process of change. You've identified many ways that you can enlist your mind and your body to help you, including things you need to do to get healthy. You've identified ways you can deal with stress and ways you can have more fun.

There's a wealth of material here, and you will want to refer back to it as a critical part of your plan. Before we move on, however, I want you to do one more thing. I want you to condense all of the most important parts of what you've written down to a single page. Some of the things you've written down probably fall into the category of *good ideas*. Others are things that you know are *essential for you*. Right now, I want you to focus on the things that are essential to you. I'm not saying don't implement the other good ideas you've written down. Some of them may end up being very important. But first, let's put down those things that seem most essential on one page. This will be your quick reference guide as you move forward.

Using the material you have personally developed in this chapter, complete the following page.

✎ PERSONAL TASK #6

Personal Relapse Prevention Plan (Condensed Version)

Here are the primary triggers I will have to avoid and routines I will have to change:

1. _____
2. _____
3. _____

Here are the primary people I will rely on to help me achieve my goals:

1. Name _____

   Phone Number _____

2. Name _____

   Phone Number _____

3. Name _____

   Phone Number _____

Here are the primary ways I will deal with triggers (by engaging the mind and the body, going and doing something fun, etc.)

1. _____
2. _____
3. _____
4. _____

Here are the primary lifestyle changes I am going to make to be healthier and better deal with stress:

1. _____

2. _____

3. _____

Here are the primary ways I am going to stay accountable for my progress:

1. _____

2. _____

3. _____

CHAPTER 13

Day One Strategies

> I am still plagued with doubts and esteem issues,
> and yes, I still feel lonely, but I am no longer masking
> these. I am confronting them and really hope to
> change these through positivism rather than hiding
> behind a hazy fog clouded and forever lost to the world.
>
> Anonymous

So, you've set a day to stop smoking, and this is it. Now what? Admittedly, making it through one day without smoking is not exactly a huge achievement. I mean, you're motivated, you're committed, and the first day you're not going through withdrawal symptoms yet, so you just need to find something else to do from now until midnight, right? Go out to eat dinner and see a late evening movie. Now you're at midnight. Well done!

OK, for some of you it doesn't feel quite that easy, and that's the point. Whether it's on the first day, or the second, or the third, you're going to need a plan. That's what you've already been working on in the previous chapter, of course.

Now you need to actually get the whole plan off the launch pad.

One of the most difficult changes you will encounter while breaking your addiction is learning new ways to cope. Maybe I shouldn't say "new ways to cope" because, in reality, they are not new at all. They are just the way most people, who do not depend on a drug to cope, get through the daily nuances of life, and the more tragic situations we sometimes experience. Marijuana plays such a role in abusers' lives that their response to tragedy and to joyous moments is the same: they "toke up" to try to cope with the former, and to celebrate the latter. When you think about it, having the same response to both is a little bit nuts, isn't it?

Even in the most tragic of situations, I have seen people cope without the use of a drug. They didn't die, and they didn't go crazy. They just hung in there until things got better. It's not that it was easy, it's just that they were able to work through the circumstance with a sober mind. Many who use drugs to cope never really have the opportunity to work through their problems. Instead of working through them, they escape from them. That's a life strategy that is doomed to failure. Why stay on that path?

For those of you who have been smoking since your teenage years, it will take you a little longer to learn new coping strategies. But everyone is capable of doing this, no matter how long you have smoked. After a few attempts to cope differently, and learning that you can handle stressful situations, you will begin to react differently to the problems and difficulties that come your way in life.

When you think about it, the purpose of many of the plans you've written down and many of the strategies you are adopting is simply to keep you occupied until the desire to smoke goes away. That is what eventually has to happen, and will happen. You're not going to be hanging on by your fingernails every day for the rest of your life, trying hard not to smoke. That would be pretty bleak, indeed. No, the desire to smoke ultimately will go away. You will remain abstinent because that's what you *want* to do.

It may seem hard to believe right now, but that *will* happen. It takes time, though. And the only way to get there is not to smoke. You have to retrain your brain. There aren't any shortcuts. But there are many ways you can help yourself through the process, and ensure you are successful.

So, today is the day you're quitting. What exactly, do you need to do first? Here are six critical actions you need to take (if you have not done so already).

Action Step 1: Remove smoking paraphernalia. Get rid of items such as pipes, papers, bongs, ashtrays, matches, lighters, and marijuana from your home and car.

If you're not willing to do this, you're simply not ready yet. If that's the case, fine. Keep reading, or maybe go back and reread Part I. When you're ready to remove your smoking paraphernalia, start right here again.

Action Step 2: Announce that you've quit. Identify the people in your life that you need to tell about your commitment, and tell them. Ask them to praise you for stopping, to not offer you pot, to provide emotional support, and not to smoke around you. This step not only helps you get the support you need; it also serves as a stake in the ground.

(Do this with the appropriate people who are close to you or who have participated in your smoking habit. I suggest not doing this with everyone else in your life, like various co-workers. With these other people in your life, let your behavior speak for itself. They'll eventually see that you're different.)

Action Step 3: Change the necessary routines. Choose which ones your need to change right now, decide on how you are going to change them, and do it.

Action Step 4: Avoid triggers. You've identified people, places, and events that are triggers for you. Start avoiding these now. If you find yourself unexpectedly in a triggering situation, walk away.

Action Step 5: Manage your cravings. Your body—including your physical brain—is going to want to smoke pot for a period of time. That's what cravings are: your body shouting "give me my pot!" Fortunately, you are the one who chooses the life you want to live; your body doesn't get the final say.

Engaging your mind, engaging your body, doing something fun, getting together with supportive people—all the things you wrote down in your relapse prevention plan—are all ways to manage your cravings. Start implementing them now. Be proactive. Don't wait until you start to feel a craving to call a friend to go to a movie or go shopping. As much as possible, do it before you feel a craving. Keep yourself busy! For the first month, at least, uncommitted time on your hands is your enemy, not your friend.

Action Step 6: Act intentionally when you are tempted. Start taking small, *immediate* actions when you start feeling tempted to smoke, when your thoughts start drifting in that direction, etc. These are things that you can do (mostly) on your own, in the moment, to redirect yourself. Which of these may be particularly useful will vary from person to person, but some of them *will* be important to you. You'll have to figure out which those are.

- **Delay the decision to give in to temptation.** This is critical. For example, if you are feeling tempted, just decide, "I'm not going to give in to that for the next 15 minutes." You're not giving yourself permission to do it after 15 minutes. You're simply declaring, "I'm not doing this for the next 15 minutes." Then, during that 15 minutes, implement one or more of the strategies that follow, or initiate one of the planning steps you wrote down, such as getting together with a friend.

- **Thought-stopping.** Tell yourself loudly to STOP and then get up and do something else. The benefit of this action is self-evident; it temporarily interrupts the drift of your mind into dangerous territory.

- **Breathe deeply.** Take several deep breaths through your nostrils (not your mouth). Focus on the fresh air entering your lungs, cleansing and nourishing your body. Let out tension with each exhalation. It's amazing how breathing as we were designed to breathe clears the mind and helps reset our emotions.

  NOTE: Maybe people find that combining thought-stopping with deep breathing, then finding something to distract themselves, is very effective.

- **Call a friend.** Talking with someone is a major distraction, which is good. If this is someone involved in helping you quit, great. Tell them you are feeling weak and you just need some support. If not, focus on them and their needs for a few minutes. Nothing gets us out of our temporary self-thinking like focusing on being there for someone else.

  NOTE: I highly recommend combining calling a friend with getting outside and taking a walk. It's amazing how this can get you past the immediate temptation, which *will* recede if you let it.

- **Carry things to put in your mouth.** Carry toothpicks, gum, mints, plastic straws, low-calorie snacks. You brain may just want your mouth to be engaged in a minor stress-relieving activity.

- **Carry objects to fiddle with.** Carry a rubber ball to squeeze, a small puzzle, a pebble, worry beads. These can be helpful momentary distractions.

- **Self-talk.** Give yourself a pep talk, remind yourself of your reasons for quitting, remind yourself of the consequences of using marijuana, challenge any wavering in your commitment to quit. Pull out your reasons for quitting list and review it.

OK, at this point you are well-equipped. You've made your commitment to stop smoking. You've done all the planning. You've gotten rid of the pot and paraphernalia. You've announced your decision to live in a new way to the appropriate people. You have your primary strategies concerning triggers, routines, support, and ways to throw yourself into healthier activities, all of which you are starting to implement.

Congratulations! That's a lot of work, and you should feel very good about having accomplished it.

What I'd like to discuss now are a few items that have a longer-term focus, but that are important to start working on now. The fact that they are longer-term doesn't mean they're not important this week. They are. It just means they will be important for many weeks to come. You'll be doing yourself a huge favor by working on these now.

Combat fatigue and low energy. If you are fatigued, you have less reserve energy to make good decisions. Be proactive in raising your energy level. Do muscle relaxations; get regular exercise, like taking a brisk walk; do things that are enjoyable and give you a sense of purpose; eat properly and get enough sleep.

Don't let insomnia derail you. Insomnia is a common withdrawal symptom, which I discuss more in Chapter 14. Don't fight being unable to sleep. Get up and do something constructive or relaxing. Read a book, watch TV, or do muscle relaxations until you feel sleepy. Remember, no one dies from losing a good night's sleep!

Think accurately about cravings and urges. I've mentioned this briefly before, but I will do so a bit more here. It's vital to have an accurate picture in your mind of what cravings are and what they are not. They are not commands that you have to obey. They are your body telling you that it wants something that you have *taught* it to want. In other words, it is a learned response. You are fully capable of making it an unlearned response. Your body won't like it when you do, but tough. Your body isn't in the driver's seat here. You are. The only way to interrupt cravings is to break the chain of responding to them. That is, don't give in. Eventually they will decrease. Respond to cravings with one or more of the action steps we just discussed. Do something to distract yourself; breathe deeply; call a friend; go for a walk; move around; start doing something else you enjoy doing. Learn to manage the urge, and you'll find that it will disappear eventually.

Think accurately about your action steps. Sometimes people seeking to quit marijuana come to look at the steps they have to take to achieve success as too burdensome. "This is too hard!" they complain. So let's address this head on and begin thinking accurately right from the start. Are any of the action steps outlined in this chapter actually difficult to do? No. In fact, they are usually simple to do. At one time or another, you've surely done them all without giving it a second thought. They simply require you to make a choice to do them. In other words, they require intentionality. By acting intentionally, over time you will develop the ability to react in healthy ways, spontaneously, on the spot. That's the goal. It simply requires some intentionality at this point on your part to get there.

✎ PERSONAL TASK #7
Complete the Self-Efficacy Questionnaire

The *Self-Efficacy Questionnaire*, taken from the *Brief Counseling for Marijuana Dependence* manual, is a way for you to rate your ability to resist the temptation to smoke marijuana in a variety of different situations. In developing your strategies to abstain, knowing what situations that would more likely to lead to relapse is important. You need to work diligently to avoid these situations or, if unavoidable, recognize the hazards of allowing the situation to affect your success.

The rating scale has a range of 1 (not at all confident) to 7 (extremely confident). Once completed, add the numbers you have chosen and then divide them by 20. This will give you your *Self-Efficacy or SE* score.

You can also complete the form on the Secret Addiction website. On the website, we have included a variety of solutions to help you avoid relapse in various situations. These will be automatically generated at the end of the questionnaire.

SELF-EFFICACY QUESTIONNAIRE

Please circle how confident you are that you could resist the temptation to smoke marijuana in the following situations.

HOW CONFIDENT ARE YOU THAT YOU COULD RESIST THE TEMPTATION TO SMOKE MARIJUANA IF YOU WERE:	NOT AT ALL CONFIDENT						EXTREMELY CONFIDENT
1. Doing monotonous work	0	1	2	3	4	5	6	7
2. Wanting to feel more confident	0	1	2	3	4	5	6	7
3. Seeing someone else smoking marijuana and enjoying it	0	1	2	3	4	5	6	7
4. Vacationing	0	1	2	3	4	5	6	7

HOW CONFIDENT ARE YOU THAT YOU COULD RESIST THE TEMPTATION TO SMOKE MARIJUANA IF YOU WERE:	NOT AT ALL CONFIDENT						EXTREMELY CONFIDENT
5. Feeling like celebrating good news or an accomplishment	0	1	2	3	4	5	6	7
6. Feeling depressed or worried	0	1	2	3	4	5	6	7
7. Drinking alcohol	0	1	2	3	4	5	6	7
8. Feeling frustrated	0	1	2	3	4	5	6	7
9. Wanting to feel better about yourself	0	1	2	3	4	5	6	7
10. Feeling angry about something or someone	0	1	2	3	4	5	6	7
11. Enjoying a pleasant social situation	0	1	2	3	4	5	6	7
12. Having time to yourself, free of responsibility	0	1	2	3	4	5	6	7
13. Using other drugs recreationally	0	1	2	3	4	5	6	7
14. Being at a party with people who are smoking marijuana	0	1	2	3	4	5	6	7
15. Feeling embarassed	0	1	2	3	4	5	6	7
16. Being in an uncomfortable social situation	0	1	2	3	4	5	6	7
17. Being offered marijuana by someone	0	1	2	3	4	5	6	7
18. Being with a spouse or close friend who is smoking marijuana	0	1	2	3	4	5	6	7
19. Being bored, with nothing to do	0	1	2	3	4	5	6	7
20. Feeling stressed out, needing to calm down	0	1	2	3	4	5	6	7

SELF-EFFICACY QUESTIONNAIRE SCORING INSTRUCTIONS

To obtain the *Self-Efficacy (SE) Score*, add the numbers circled for each item and divide by the total number answered (the denominator should be 20 unless an item was skipped).

SE Score: _____

Items circled as 1, 2, or 3 indicate that the particular situations would be more difficult to resist and would affect your ability to remain abstinent. Devise strategies to avoid or minimize these situations. As I stated above, on the website, we have included a variety of solutions to help you avoid relapse in various situations.

CHAPTER 14

What to Expect After Day One

I have taken the first step. I have quit for 24 hours now and I am on day 2. My desire is strong and I will continue to be marijuana free. However, my concern lies in my feelings of being lost or displaced. My entire social scene has been built around marijuana use. I feel extremely isolated and bored. From past experience, these feelings only make me want to get high more. Now, I know I can go out and make sober friends, but I got to tell you . . . I am not fun to be around right now. Emotionally I am all over the place.

Anonymous

Day Two

Well, how do you feel today? For most of you, this is somewhat of an accomplishment, isn't it? How long has it been since you actually went a day without smoking? Maybe to some it sounds a bit silly to be so pleased about one full day without smoking, but believe me, I know how important this is and what an accomplishment you are feeling.

You might have a slight sense of confidence that you can actually do this. And yes, you are correct. You *can* do this. Better yet, you *will* do this. Today will be pleasantly different simply because you can experience the day without that familiar feeling of cloudiness from the previous day of smoking and, for some of you, overeating.

But let's not get too far ahead of ourselves yet. It is just the second day and, for some, you are still riding "high" on the emotional resolve to quit. In fact, your body doesn't really miss the marijuana yet, because it is still lingering in your system in significant quantities. Remember, weed eliminates itself from the body rather slowly. Although the fun psychoactive effects are no longer active, those little cannabinoid receptors in your body are still enjoying the party you had the day before yesterday.

However, for some, the second day is a little more difficult. That's what is tricky about this drug. Everyone's experience can be dramatically different. Trust me, if you are experiencing more difficulty today, it's not because you are weaker than those who seem to be doing fine. It is because your experience, your circumstance, or your physiology might simply be dissimilar. Don't worry. Those people who are getting a little boastful today will eventually endure the bite of the temptation monster. It's inevitable.

So, if you are one those individuals who are experiencing a little irritability, take it easy. The days do get easier and easier. I promise. If you make the wrong choice and call your dealer, then there is no telling when you might gain the strength or desire to start reading this book again. Six months to one year would be my guess. Are you ready to go through that process again? You have already made a commitment to yourself and have made it through the mental preparation to begin this journey. Now, stop the destructive thinking and suck it up.

So what can you expect to encounter the remainder of the first week? That's what this chapter is about. You know the old saying:

Knowledge is power.

That saying *really* applies here. If you know what to expect, you can handle it. You *can* handle it!

The Dreaded Withdrawals

"I am ready to live. Yes, withdrawals suck. My headaches are a nuisance and the night sweats are gross. The dream intensity thing is a bit odd, but life must be confronted with honesty. I am ready to experience pain, with honesty. I am ready put my face forward knowing full well that it is me without the 'crutch'." ANONYMOUS

This may be news to some, but withdrawal symptoms are for real. For some reason, some people want to continue to deny this. Maybe they think that physical withdrawal for marijuana is not as much of an issue as psychological withdrawal, and for some individuals that is undoubtedly true. But the vast majority of people who have attempted to quit have experienced physical withdrawal symptoms. Just read any blog about marijuana abstinence and that becomes obvious. People aren't making these symptoms up. In fact, the symptoms can be uncomfortable enough to drive some individuals to re-continue their use simply to avoid withdrawals. That's *not* the path we want to take! Thankfully, most withdrawal symptoms are short-lived, lasting no more than three to four weeks.

So how do we deal with withdrawal symptoms? Many helps for this are included in chapters 20 and 21, and I recommend that you review these immediately. They really will help.

But the most important thing in dealing with withdrawals has to do with the way in which you view them. You can approach this with fear, frustration and misery, or you can recognize the withdrawals for what they are; a temporary cleansing of the body through symptoms that, for the most part, are no different than the common flu. Having the flu is no fun, but for almost all healthy individuals, you have it, you suffer for a bit, you recover, and life goes on. In other words, it's endurable! No one questions that.

Well, marijuana withdrawals are the same way.

Allen Carr addresses this in his book, *The Easy Way to Stop Smoking*. He's talking specifically about cigarette smoking, but the principle is exactly the same. When discussing the withdrawal symptoms of cigarette smoking with a client, he offers the suggestion: "You can have the flu for five days, after which you will be a happy non-smoker for the rest of your life."

Carr comments concerning a smoker confronted with such a choice:

> He would jump at the opportunity. Even when we have genuine flu, we feel we can cope with the situation. However, if you press smokers who are trying to quit to be more specific about the pain they are suffering, they come out with statements such as: 'I keep breaking out in a sweat,' or 'I can't concentrate or sleep at night.' We point out to them that athletes break out in a sweat every time they perform and that we all have periods when we can't concentrate or sleep at night. We don't seem to regard these things as a great tragedy, so where's the problem? They find it hard to explain.

Of course, some of the withdrawals we experience when quitting marijuana are slightly different than when quitting cigarettes (such as intense dreaming), but many are the same.

The following is a list of the common withdrawal symptoms of someone who has been smoking marijuana heavily for a sustained period of time.

- Depressed mood
- Decreased appetite
- Irritability
- Increased aggression

- Increased anger
- Strange dreams
- Nervousness/anxiety
- Headaches
- Craving
- Shakiness
- Restlessness
- Sweating
- Sleep difficulty
- Stomach pains
- Nausea
- Constipation

In one study, adolescents presenting for outpatient substance-abuse treatment completed a questionnaire reporting the presence and severity of withdrawal symptoms during past periods of cannabis abstinence. More than three-quarters of the sample indicated that they had experienced multiple symptoms, and over one-third reported four or more symptoms that occurred at a moderate or greater severity (Vandrey et al., 2005). A similar study of adults revealed that withdrawal symptoms for them were worse than for adolescents.

It helps tremendously to realize beforehand that some of these withdrawal symptoms are just going to have to happen, like the sweating or the strange dreams. Physiologically, you can't stop the body from responding this way. The suggestions provided in Chapter 20 will you help you tremendously, but you are going to need a little perseverance and some toughness to get through this part. It's kind of like having ACL repair surgery on your knee. It's no fun, it's going to be unpleasant, it's going to hurt some after the surgery, and the rehab is going to be uncomfortable. *The surgeon tells you all of that beforehand.* You know what? People have ACL repair surgery all the time. Why do they choose to put themselves through all of it? Because it's better than limping around the rest of their lives!

The truth is, kicking marijuana is no different. You have a choice. You can keep limping through life—much worse than limping through life, actually, because marijuana is not only harming you, it's harming those you love—or you can accept the discomfort and get on with it. Almost no one with a torn ACL says, "You know, I think I'd rather just live with this the rest of my life." That would be ridiculous! Instead, you just go through the surgery and get it over with.

The good news is this: most of the withdrawals are gone after two weeks and the rest by the end of the first month. I'm serious.

The reality is that some of the symptoms listed are directly linked to your attitude about not getting what you want. That seems to be the biggest problem . . . desiring the very thing you can't have. The very fact that you're having that problem means that you're not 100% on board with stopping. Many of us know deep inside that it needs to end, but there is still that lingering love affair with the way things are. I would say that most people in this position still have not made a 100% change in their attitude toward smoking pot. That doesn't mean that you can't accomplish this task. You can! However, it can make for an intense first few weeks with the moodiness and cravings.

There is a distinct difference between someone who desires to quit and someone who really knows they are done. In people who know they are done, there is no pondering the thought of "only on the weekends," or hanging onto their paraphernalia "just in case." You typically find this type of resolve in individuals who have failed many times at their attempts to quit, or people who are experiencing something in their life that is much greater than the pleasure they derive from smoking.

The more common of the two, obviously, are those that have failed miserably many times and understand the difficulty of really quitting. These individuals do not take it lightly and are much more committed and serious about the process. If you are going through this for the first or second time, take notice of this group. You can either make the decision to stop now and suck it up through the very temporary withdrawals, or you can be searching for new methods to help you stop the habit ten years from now. Once again, it's your choice.

So, let's get specific about some of the more prevalent withdrawal symptoms. What can you possibly expect?

Sleeping Problems

What's that? You say you can't sleep? This is the most common symptom of marijuana withdrawal by most accounts, and it can be a miserable one. Think about it. In a dark, quiet room where you lie awake, nothing to think about except how pissed off you are that you can't sleep and that if you only had . . . stop it! I have written about the benefits of the amino acid 5-HTP as a natural aid to help you sleep in Chapter 20. Get some. Take it. It's very effective. Look, sleeping problems are no fun. I totally admit that. But they will pass. I promise.

Night Sweats

Night sweats are very common and have, more than likely, already begun. I always hear stories of individuals constantly changing their sheets because of the profuse sweating they experience. The consensus concerning night sweats seems to be that your body is simply beginning to go through a detoxification process.

This is a good thing. Although there are many of routes of detoxification, such as the liver or the blood, the skin is a major contributor to eliminating wastes from the body and sweating is a good way to push these toxins out. (I cover detoxification briefly and ways to "slowly" assist the body in ridding itself of these pollutants in Chapter 20.)

However, I believe one more dynamic is at play. I believe the increase in body temperature is due to the temperature regulator of the brain, the hypothalamus, making an attempt to normalize on its own. The hypothalamus is loaded with cannabinoid receptors to which the THC in marijuana will attach itself. Now that it is freed of these external cannabinoids, it begins the process of self-regulating, but in a very imbalanced manner. This is probably why we hear of some people getting cold at times, too.

Although I don't recommend taking supplements to speed up the detoxification process, sweating during exercise does promote detoxification, and I highly recommend that. Doing exercise is also important for many other reasons which I discuss in the Chapter 20 section, "Get Your Body in Motion!"

Fortunately, as with sleeping problems, night sweats will pass.

Irritability

This symptom may seem odd. I have heard many times that people return to smoking because they felt that they were too difficult to be around during this phase. Sometimes, they deceive themselves by saying they are going back to smoking for the sake of their friends or family. Of course, if a spouse or significant other makes this suggestion, you will have a difficult time achieving your goal, because you are obviously not getting support from the people you need it from the most. They are supposed to be supporting the recovery with you, and, therefore, need to make a few sacrifices in order to help you succeed.

Thankfully, you probably have their support. Therefore, it's really your choice to use this as an excuse to go back to smoking. Remember, good excuses always make sense in the moment. Why would anyone in their right mind take the blame for their own failure, especially when a good excuse is so conveniently nearby?

Keep in mind, it is always *your* decision to start smoking again and not the excuse you are using at the moment. From this day forward you are going to have to take responsibility.

The truth is that irritability is just part of the deal. *Everybody* gets irritable. Personally, I don't know many people who don't get at least a little cranky when they can't get what they want. Throw years of habit and a bit of craving into the mix, and you'd better watch out! If you think about it, this is how three-year-olds act when they don't get their way. They whine, they pout, and they throw a fit. It's time to move emotionally past age three. OK, you're irritable. That's normal. Just accept it, try to not make life miserable for everyone around you, and move on. You won't be irritable forever.

Following the advice on the various supplements I have recommended in Chapter 20 can help you tremendously. However, if you are on the high end of the aggressiveness or irritability scale, you may need extra help. See the discussion in Chapter 15 on anger management. Also, strongly consider the additional helps I discuss in Chapter 21. Some of them can hugely assist with this issue.

Dreams

"The one thing that I have definitely experienced and I never thought it would be like this is the dreams. I have not been able to remember my dreams for as long as I can remember, then in the last couple of days, the dreams have been so vivid and so intense they have actually awakened me with a startle."

ANONYMOUS

If you have begun to have vivid dreams, this is very normal. Dreams typically begin around the seventh day and can last up to four or more weeks. These dreams can be so intense and terrifying that they can lead some people back to smoking. I know this from personal experience. The dreaming has to take place, but the reason they are so frightening is because the nervous system is under stress. It's the same reason why we may have nightmares when eating heavy meats before bed. You can partially alleviate this by simply taking an over-the-counter amino acid supplement called 5-HTP.

5-HTP usually comes in 100 mg tablets, and you should take 200 mg per day. I recommend taking one 100 mg dose in the morning, and one in the evening before bed. I would suggest following this regimen for about two months. Taking 5-HTP will also assist you with the irritability and depression.

5-HTP is not like a prescription anti-depressant. The prescription medications come with their own set of repercussions and should be avoided, if possible. Nor is it a sign of weakness to resort to this type of ammunition. You could tough it out, as many people attempt to do, but if dreams and related symptoms cause some people to fail, then why not utilize these options? Bear in mind, I am not promoting any sort of prescription medication, but rather a natural supplement that can be bought anywhere. I have included more information on this and other amino acids in Chapter 20 and also at secretaddiction.org.

Seven Days and Counting

Well done! When you reach the end of the first week, it is your moment to sit back, take a deep breath, and think about what you have accomplished. You have just finished the first of many milestones that lie ahead of you. The first week is the biggest of them all. Why? First, because it is the most difficult in terms of withdrawal symptoms. You are now well into the night sweats, sleeping difficulties, and maybe some of you have already begun the intense dreaming. And you've endured.

Another reason this one-week milestone is important is because you made a decision to stop smoking, and you stuck to it. Congratulate yourself on a job well done. Be proud of what you have accomplished. Go out today feeling more confident, and looking people in the eye when you speak to them, because you are a more powerful individual. There are not many people who could have mustered up the courage to do what you have just done.

But remember, confidence and cockiness are not the same. Don't start jumping up and down as if you have defeated this thing. We still have work to do. You still have a long way to go.

Nevertheless, you have made it through the beginning stages of becoming a non-smoker. How does that sound? You, a "non-smoker!" That's going to be a shocker to some people, isn't it? Well, you and everyone else need to get used to it, because that's the way it's going to be. In fact, I don't want you to be just a "non-smoker." You need to become a different person, and with the right attitude and the right amount of effort, you can do it.

After the first week, some of you might be feeling weak or starting to periodically experience cravings. Realize this: the subconscious helps drive many of your actions. That's the way humans are wired. We don't have to be slaves to it, but we do have to take it into account. At any given moment you might pick up the pipe and smoke without thinking it through, until after it has happened. Simply be aware of that dynamic and be prepared to handle it.

If you are feeling a little ambivalent or unsure about your decision right now, don't worry. What you are feeling is quite common, especially this early in the game. You are still attached to smoking, and you are attempting to change a pattern that has developed over many years. Give yourself time.

Honestly, one week is the point when many people decide it is too hard, and they return to the same old habits. Why would they make such a decision, after they've cleared the first (and highest) hurdle? Because they are thinking the wrong way. They haven't learned to manage their thoughts.

So, before proceeding any further, let's turn to that topic.

✎ PERSONAL TASK #8
CUDIT – R (Repeated)

Did you take the Cannabis Use Disorder Identification Test – Revised (CUDIT-R) at the end of Chapter 6? If not, take it now. Or if you did take it before, retake it now. It assesses whether a person's marijuana smoking is causing serious problems in his life. Take this brief questionnaire about your marijuana usage before you stopped perhaps a few days ago and honestly ask yourself the question, "Can I afford to take this attempt to quit lightly?"

Cannabis Use Disorder Identification Test – Revised (CUDIT-R)

Have you used any cannabis over the past six months?   YES / NO

If YES, please answer the following questions about your cannabis use.

Circle the response that is most correct for you in relation to your cannabis use *over the past six months.*

1. How often do you use cannabis?				
Never	Monthly or less	2-4 times a month	2-3 times a week	4 or more times a week
0	1	2	3	4

2. How many hours were you "stoned" on a typical day when you had been using cannabis?				
Less than 1	1 or 2	3 or 4	5 or 6	7 or more
0	1	2	3	4

3. How often during the past 6 months did you find that you were not able to stop using cannabis once you had started?				
Never	Less than monthly	Monthly	Weekly	Daily or almost daily
0	1	2	3	4

4. How often during the past 6 months did you fail to do what was normally expected from you because of using cannabis?				
Never	Less than monthly	Monthly	Weekly	Daily or almost daily
0	1	2	3	4

5. **How often in the past 6 months have you devoted a great deal of your time to getting, using, or recovering from cannabis?**

Never	Less than monthly	Monthly	Weekly	Daily or almost daily
0	1	2	3	4

6. **How often in the past 6 months have you had a problem with your memory or concentration after using cannabis?**

Never	Less than monthly	Monthly	Weekly	Daily or almost daily
0	1	2	3	4

7. **How often do you use cannabis in situations that could be physically hazardous, such as driving, operating machinery, or caring for children?**

Never	Less than monthly	Monthly	Weekly	Daily or almost daily
0	1	2	3	4

8. **Have you ever thought about cutting down, or stopping, your use of cannabis?**

Never	Yes, but not in the past 6 months	Yes, during the past 6 months
0	2	4

This scale is in the public domain and is free to use with appropriate citation:
Adamson SJ, Kay-Lambkin FJ, Baker AL, Lewin TJ, Thornton L. Kelly BJ, and Sellman JD. (2010). An improved Brief Measure of Cannabis Misuse: The Cannabis Use Disorders Identification Test – Revised (CUDIT-R). *Drug and Alcohol Dependence* 110:137-143.

This questionnaire was designed for self administration and is scored by adding each of the 8 items:
  – Questions 1-7 are scored on a 0-4 scale.
  – Question 8 is scored 0, 2 or 4.

Scores of 8 or more indicate hazardous cannabis use, while scores of 12 or more indicate a possible cannabis use disorder for which further intervention may be required.

CHAPTER 15

Managing Your Thoughts and Emotions

The thought itself isn't the problem; it's how people cope with their thoughts. If people learn to dismiss this thinking from their minds whenever it appears, recognize it for what it is, or counter it with a challenging thought, it need not lead to a relapse.

Brief Counseling for Marijuana Dependence

Quit Your "Stinking Thinking"

It all starts with our thinking. Everything does. You have heard the saying that thoughts lead to actions. How could it be any other way? It was your thinking, or your attitudes, that convinced you it was acceptable to smoke in the first place. And it has allowed you to continue to smoke, even when you knew that it was causing more harm than good.

Unfortunately, most people's thinking is negative. However, it doesn't have to be a so-called negative thought that convinces people to smoke. Many times, it's simply the thought that we need to reward ourselves. Whether it is good thoughts or bad thoughts,

we need to recognize the patterns that lead to smoking and identify the lies embedded deep within them.

Furthermore, many of your thoughts are so subtle, or as some
would say, subconscious, that you don't even notice the impact
they have on your actions. They can be so automatic and repetitious that you slowly move down the path of relapse with no signs
or warnings. Luckily, when you examine your thoughts, you can
begin to change your actions, leading to a more positive and productive life.

Is it easy? The simple answer is no. It is not easy. For better
or worse, you have been trained by the most influential people
in your life (like your parents) to think in many of the ways that
you do, and you have behaved this way for almost as long as you
have been breathing. Even though it is not easy, per se, the methods of eliminating patterns are very simple. The secret (and, for
most people, the difficult part) is simply remaining consistent with
these methods.

There are two types of thoughts we need to discuss. The first
are the self-defeating thoughts that attack our self-esteem or self-
worth. These can, and most likely will, lead you back toward the
need to escape the uncomfortable feelings they produce. The
second are the thought-cravings that come regularly in the beginning. Just about everyone who stops using thinks about using.
Thinking about using is not a problem, provided you don't act on
the thoughts. Sometimes, of course, that is easier said than done. I
will explain in a moment.

So, first let's tackle those negative thoughts that not only drive us
back to smoking, but are also the ones responsible for most people
not reaching their potential in life. We are driven daily by these
thoughts, and as I said earlier, most of these are negative for the vast
majority of people. Many self-help gurus promote the effectiveness
of reciting positive affirmations, out loud and with emotion, to help
drive your subconscious into a more constructive way of thinking

and to eliminate the negative "stinking thinking." Positive affirmations have worked and continue to work for many people.

When I first began to study self-improvement or motivational topics, I encountered a method called the "Delete Technique." It stated that when you have one of those negative thoughts, recognize it, and then say the words "delete, delete, delete." If that description sounds a bit too simplistic, it is. I never really found this method to be very effective! I figured that by saying those three words, my thought would magically disappear. It never did. Until I finally realized I was missing the most important component of this technique.

Recognizing the negative thought was only the first part of the equation. The second component I had missed was not only recognizing the thought itself, but the lie I was telling myself. Most of the time we are just deceiving ourselves with our negative thoughts. In the famous book, *The Art of War*, Sun Tzu says that "all warfare is based on deception."

Your thoughts have been deceiving you, and winning the war for too long. In fact, it probably wasn't your thought to begin with. It was someone else's thought. You were just gullible enough to believe it. Now that you know it is not the truth, you need to replace it with what is true. Reading written positive affirmations aloud can help, but keep in mind that you are virtually affirming thoughts every minute of the day. So, consistently recognizing and replacing the ones that do not serve you well is extremely important.

If the replaced thought, or positive affirmation, still feels like you are stretching the truth, then try the "but" method until saying good things to yourself becomes second nature. Here's how it works: anytime you feel yourself thinking negatively, use the word "but" and point out positive aspects. For example, "I *feel* like such a failure, *but* I am choosing positive changes that will bring success."

This leads us into the second topic: thought-cravings. As I mentioned earlier, these thoughts will come very frequently in the first few weeks. There is no doubt that you are going into battle. Fighting your way through this is a daunting task, which will wear you down and eventually take you over. Sun Tzu writes,

> When you engage in actual fighting, if victory is long coming, then your weapons will grow dull and your ardor will be dampened. . . . Hence to fight and conquer in all your battles is not supreme excellence; supreme excellence consists in breaking the enemy's resistance without fighting.

Thought-cravings, most of the time, come in tiny packages. At the beginning we shrug it off as an insignificant thought to be dismissed and ignored. After all, you are done with smoking, right? But these little thought-craving devils do not like to be ignored, so they go and find some more of their little thought-craving friends and begin to attack you.

After a while, you can no longer ignore these thoughts, and you begin to take notice. The mistake we make, when we become aware of them, is to start fighting. The fighting is minimal at first, because the thoughts are only making us a little uncomfortable. But the more uncomfortable we get, the more the thoughts come, and the more we fight. This is the point that Sun Tzu was making when he said, "Your weapons will grow dull and your ardor will be dampened."

Although these thought-cravings are small individually, they accumulate and eventually smother you, until you give in. It makes me uncomfortable even writing about this, having experienced it before. Thankfully, understanding your enemy is the greatest weapon of all.

From now on, do not ignore these thoughts when they arrive, but rather take the time to examine them, understand the deception or lie they have been telling you all of these years, and then replace it with the truth: the truth being who you want to be or who you are becoming. There is no use in struggling unnecessarily.

Of course, there will be challenges, but much of this is about facing reality, and nothing can be real if we are constantly being deceived.

OK, let's get specific. Following are some specific strategies that will help you manage your thoughts about using marijuana. This list was derived from the *Brief Counseling for Marijuana Dependence* manual. I have changed the explanations slightly, and added a few comments of my own. (Some of these, of course, have been mentioned previously in briefer form. A little repetition of these suggestions doesn't hurt at this stage.)

Challenge your thoughts. Use other thoughts to challenge your old thoughts about using (recognize and replace). An important aspect of "replacing" thoughts about using is to avoid visualizing what you are not going to do, and instead picture a new behavior that you can do. You might try developing a mental picture of the new behavior when the old habit pops into your mind.

A few examples of replacements would be:

- "I cannot get a little high without increasing my risk of using more."
- "I don't have to use marijuana to unwind after work."
- "Many people do it every day without smoking so I can find other ways."
- "I can have good times without smoking."
- "It may feel strange at first, but in time I'll feel more comfortable."

I can't overemphasize the importance of doing this. Creating a new reality starts in the mind. Learning how to visualize the "new you" with a clear mental picture is the foundation of this process.

List and recall the benefits of not using. Thoughts about the personal benefits of abstinence can weaken excuses for using. Benefits you can think about include better physical health, improved family life, job stability, more money for recreation and paying bills, increased self-esteem, and self-control. It is important to pay attention to these positive aspects and the progress you are making. *Do not* focus on what you are giving up.

Carry a card with you listing these benefits. Add items as you think of them, and review them regularly. On the website we have created a template for your Benefits Card. I encourage you to carry the card. You never know when the moment of temptation will arrive.

Recall and list unpleasant using experiences. Recall the pain, fear, embarrassment, and negative feelings associated with using marijuana. Make a list of unpleasant experiences, such as memory problems, lack of motivation, procrastination, legal problems, withdrawal, paranoia, and sleep disturbances on the back of the Benefits Card. Read the card regularly. Counteract any positive thoughts about using with the negative aspects of using, and the benefits of abstinence. Visualize the possible smoking episode to the end as well as the detrimental consequences associated with using marijuana.

The past, and especially the memory of a negative event, becomes part of our DNA to help prevent us from repeating something that might be harmful. It is important to learn from the past in order to progress to the future. To dwell in the past is one thing, but to productively remember it for sake of making positive change is another.

NOTE: I highly recommend going back to your "Reasons for Quitting" questionnaire to remind yourself as to why you wanted to take this route of making positive changes to your life in the first place.

Find distractions. Think about something pleasant, like holiday plans, vacation spots, loved ones, relaxation, or hobbies. Focus on a task you want to get done.

Leave or change the situation. Try a different activity, such as a hobby or physical exercise. It is best to leave a situation that might induce a "thought craving." You have built a life around people, places, and things that you associate with smoking. If leaving is not an option, you need to learn refusal skills. These are all a part of the tough decisions you will have to make during this process. You can do it. Trust me.

Call your supporter of friend. Your supporter or friend is like the good angel sitting on your shoulder. Use them as much as possible. This person has made a commitment to you and will be there whenever you call, no matter what.

Use self-talk. "Self-talk" refers to constructive things you can say to yourself that replace negative thoughts. We talk to ourselves all the time. Our thoughts have a powerful effect on how we feel and how we choose to act. One way to be sure negative thoughts don't sabotage your effort to quit is to learn how to recognize them and challenge them effectively. Constructive self-talk is an effective way of coping with thoughts that make staying away from marijuana difficult.

I will close this section with a powerful quote from Dr. Larry Markson that pretty much says it all concerning managing your thoughts:

> Whatever thoughts you fill your mind with and allow it to dwell upon will become your reality. Your unlimited power lies in your ability to control your thoughts. Remember that your life and the circumstances or things going on around you are a mirror of the thoughts that you allow to dominate your mind.
>
> DR. LARRY MARKSON, *TALKING TO YOURSELF IS NOT CRAZY*

Now, let's turn to a topic that is vital for so many marijuana abusers.

Anger Management: It's Really Important

"When angry, count to 10 before you speak. If very angry, a hundred." THOMAS JEFFERSON

Anger is something we all have to deal with, whether we are smoking or not. It's just part of being human. When we are frustrated about something, unhappy with something or someone, when our feelings get hurt, when things aren't going as we want them to, or when someone criticizes us, we can get angry.

At the right times and in the right amounts, anger can be a very healthy emotional response. If someone is being treated unjustly, for instance, anger is an appropriate response. It can spur us toward the necessary action to correct a situation.

Unfortunately, the times when our anger actually helps a situation are usually infrequent. Having an initial feeling of anger about something is normal. Stewing in it, constantly thinking about it, lashing out at someone because of it, being irritable all day from it—none of these ever helps matters. And, usually, those are the things that we let anger do to us and those close to us.

More often than not, anger acts against us. It poisons our thinking, damages our relationships, causes us to bypass opportunities, and, in the long run, it can ruin our health. When we let anger do these things to us, we are not acting in our own best interest. We need a better way to handle it.

Part of being human is accepting the fact that things in life often don't go the way we want them to. If you were the only person on the planet, your control over things might be greater. But you also might be a little lonely! People often don't act how we would like them to. Situations arise that we don't like. That's part of life. We can either accept that and learn to respond in positive ways, or we can go through life being mad.

We often can't control our circumstances, but we can always choose to control how we respond to them. If we let circumstances or people negatively affect us mentally and emotionally, we are giving away our power. As smokers, we tried to take power, our sense of being in control, through pot. But smoking pot never actually gave us back our power. That was an illusion. Smoking was simply an escape. It actually caused us to give away more of our power.

The solution to taking back our power, and handling anger, is having an attitude of mental and emotional detachment. This doesn't mean we don't care about or ignore what others say or do, or that we are insensitive to them. It means that we have the attitude of, "I am going to choose my own inner reality; I will respect you and take into account what you are saying, but you do not get to choose my inner reality for me. I choose what I think, the mood I am in, and how I can appropriately respond."

Letting other people or our circumstances dictate how we think, or what we feel, is very disempowering. When we do so, we are at their mercy.

Often we let the smallest things cause us to get angry and ruin our day, or at least part of it. We let a minor event—a look we interpret a certain way, a stray remark, someone cutting us off in traffic, someone not answering a question to our satisfaction—control our thoughts and feelings. We get angry. We snap back at them, argue with them, or worse.

We don't have to live life this way! Life is a lot more pleasant when we don't. And, for former pot smokers, it is vitally important that we don't. For so many of us, anger is a significant trigger that will start playing with our minds: "This isn't fair! Look how you were treated! You deserve a break from this injustice. Just one smoke. You deserve a release from all these negative feelings. Just one smoke."

We need to be proactive in not letting anger lead us into that trap. The best way to do that is to train ourselves to have peace of mind. It will not only help us avoid relapse; it will enrich our lives beyond what we expected. Teaching ourselves to have peace of mind is key to overcoming anxiety in our lives, dealing with stress, rooting our negative thinking, and enabling us to respond to situations calmly, with our thoughts and emotions under control. Wouldn't we all rather live that way?

To achieve this kind of peace of mind, and to avoid the destructive effects of anger, we have to develop mental and emotional detachment. Many books have been written about developing peace of mind, and numerous resources are available to help on that pursuit. I recommend some on the website.

To get started on handling anger, here are a few simple suggestions from Remez Sasson, the author of *Peace of Mind in Daily Life, Will Power and Self Discipline, Visualize and Achieve* and *Affirmations: Words of Power*. (You can visit his website at www.successconsciousness.com.)

1. At least once a day, devote several minutes to thinking about how much your life would be better without anger.

2. When you feel anger arising in you, start breathing deeply and slowly.

3. In addition to breathing deeply, count slowly from one to ten. This will delay your anger and weaken it.

4. Drink some water. It has a calming effect on the body.

5. Try to be more patient, no matter how difficult it might be.

6. Be more tolerant toward people, even toward people you don't like.

7. Everyone is entitled to his/her opinion. You can disagree with people, but still maintain tact and diplomacy.

8. Choose to react calmly and peacefully in every situation. Keep practicing, regardless of how many times you lose control and get angry.

9. Positive thinking makes it easier to disregard remarks and behavior that otherwise could cause anger.

10. Always try to manifest some self-control, self-discipline and more common sense.

11. Don't take everything too seriously.

12. Find reasons to laugh more often.

This list from Remez is a great start. Another tool I have found very helpful is the "I Love List," which helps solidify in our thoughts and emotions the positive change we are making. It is your next Personal Task.

✎ PERSONAL TASK #9

The "I Love List"

I came across this once and thought it was very insightful. The more time you have away from the pot habit, the more items you will probably have for this list, and the stronger you will likely feel about them. Nevertheless, this is a great exercise no matter where you are in the process. This list can be very useful, when you are tempted, in stopping you from deceiving yourself into letting smoking back into your life.

You may not be able to relate to all of these, but you will probably relate to a good many. Read through this list out loud. Use a highlighter to mark the ones that are most meaningful to you personally. Add to the list at the bottom, both now and as the weeks pass. Read through it again out loud. Read through it out loud often to cement in your mind the vital things you are *gaining* in your life by your decision to stop smoking.

THE "I LOVE LIST"

- I love thinking and speaking coherently.
- I love not having the munchies.
- I love being a better parent.
- I love eating healthy food and sweating out the toxins.
- I love drinking lots of good water.
- I love not having this secret from people who don't smoke.
- I love being able to sleep without smoking.
- I love saving money for other things that are important to me.
- I love catching up with friends I haven't seen in years.
- I love remembering.

- I love keeping my word to friends and family.
- I love that they notice I look healthier and sound happier.
- I love talking to and spending quality time with my

  _____ .
- I love looking to the future and making plans.
- I love breathing easier; each breath makes my lungs cleaner.
- I love being awake during the day.
- I love that I have plans, and that I will keep them.
- I love that I have a social life that extends beyond the couch.
- I love speaking in sentences without forgetting what I was saying.
- I love being free to do what I want without worrying if the bowl is full.
- I love not waiting to score.
- I love having time to think and ponder about humans and our souls.
- I love feeling my body is lighter and my mind is clearer.
- I love that the house is clean enough to invite people over!
- I love feeling better about myself.
- I love being free.
- I love that I LOVE being free.

- _____

- _____

- _____

- _____

- _____

- _____

- _____

- _____

- _____

CHAPTER 16

Triggers and Relapses

I was a little down yesterday because I had the
urge to use last night. I felt a little guilty. But what
an awesome feeling to know my string of clean
time is still intact. Maybe I needed a little shake
up just to remind me that I have to stay focused
all the time and not let the complacency set in.

Anonymous

There are so many different triggers, big and small, that
require us to be careful. Boredom and stress were mine.
Although, I admit that the smoking created much of my stress.
And since I was stressed, I didn't really feel like doing anything,
which led to me feeling bored. Rather than lying around and feeling guilty for doing nothing and being stressed, I would smoke
more. It doesn't make sense, does it? Our reasons never really do
in the long run.

This habit is difficult to forget, and everyone is subjected to
provoking triggers periodically. But simply being aware of these
is your shield, so to speak. Identify your triggers, or what it is that
tempts you to smoke. Is it boredom, stress, or are you seeking to
enhance your creativity? Many triggers are personal characteristics
we simply try to cover up with smoking so we do not have to deal

with them. They may include procrastination, lack of motivation, poor financial habits (a big one for stress smokers), etc.

As mentioned in a previous chapter, you need to work on you, *as a person*, and not just as a smoker. There was a reason why you became a human chimney in the first place. However, these underlying issues are not the only thing that will steer you back to your old ways. There will be memories of the euphoric associations and habits you have attached to smoking in the past, such as how it makes food taste better or movies funnier. You will miss these moments from time to time in the beginning. We can't deny that smoking elevates our mental interpretation of these things, but you need to remember that life *is* enjoyable without the artificial stimulation.

At the beginning stages of quitting, our high motivation provides a newfound strength to abstain. Sooner or later, this sensation wanes, and we ultimately have to experience these temptations on our own. We will all have an opportunity to pass or fail when this test arrives. Do not feel guilty when these temptations do come, because this is natural. Be happy if you succeed. Be resilient if you temporarily fail. Always remember that these feelings you experience are not you, but just lingering memories of who you used to be.

With all addictions, you develop a revolving mindset of stimulus and response: stress-escape; anger-escape; hurt-escape; joy-escape. Whatever it may be, it is a cycle that is not worth repeating. Big things, little things—they can all set you back if you do not deal with them in a positive and proactive way. Emotions often throw addicts for a loop.

My nemesis was stress. Stressful situations don't go away, nor do many of our emotions. It is how we deal with them that matters in recovery. Many times, when you become overconfident that you have defeated the habit, life has a funny way of throwing you a "trigger" to test your resolve.

Making the right decision *every time* is the main ingredient as to whether you make it to the last chapter of this book, or not.

That may sound impossible. It isn't. To quit smoking, you eventually have to choose every time not to smoke. That's pretty obvious. Your decisions, your choices, your life. "Doing what you need to do may not always make you happy, but it will make you great!"

Do not let ANYTHING become a reason to break your chain of clean time. You have to make the commitment that NOTHING can be an excuse to use. It is an imperative mindset to establish for continued success. However, and I say this with caution, relapses are common, and they have to dealt with in a constructive way, in a non-negative fashion.

According to psychologist Saul Shiffman, there are three different categories or techniques to resisting urges; cognitive, behavioral, and social. To succeed in the face of the urges that come and go, you have to think right, behave right, and socialize right.

All of these come down to choices that you make, and not someone else. You are the one responsible for the consequences of your decisions, good or bad. You are the one who decides to remember the negative consequences of when you smoked daily, or only recall the so-called positive. You make the decision to resist the urges with alternative activities or sheer determination. And, ultimately, you are the one who makes the decision to contact someone who supports you and truly cares about your success, or conversely a person who merely stands to make a $10 profit on a bag of weed.

If you happen to relapse, it is not the end of the road. You do not have to spiral out of control as many people do. But you do need to understand that, for most people, once that resolve has been broken, it gets easier to break a second time. As Stanton Peele wrote in his book, *7 Tools to Beat Addiction*, "You become a victim of your own inertia." Peele elaborates:

> It is important to recognize your own power in fighting addiction. Relapse is not an unfortunate event that happens to you; it is a series of bad choices that you make. The key is

to realize that even if you slip, you do not have to descend in a free fall to a complete relapse.

Believe it or not, some of you who have just read the previous paragraph may have been subtly tempted to think that it would be all right to have just "one" smoke. That is exactly the thinking and behavior that requires correcting, that led us into all the negative consequences in the first place. Accounting for relapses does not give you the green light to give in temporarily simply because you think you are strong enough to pick yourself up and keep moving forward! If you were really that strong, the thought wouldn't even enter your mind.

The point I am making is that you shouldn't beat yourself up over a misstep in the recovery process. Many people get out of control after a momentary weakness because of the guilt and failure they associate with the slip. Most people unnecessarily fail after giving in, but that doesn't have to happen. However, by far the easiest and most effective action is to not go down that road in the first place. Why intentionally choose to make things harder on yourself?

In his poem of the same name, Robert Frost famously says he took the road less traveled, and that made all the difference. Many people have traveled down the road more traveled—the one that keeps you stuck where you are. Don't take that road! Focus, and keep moving on. You won't regret it!

Preventing Relapse: 15 Things to Avoid

"Shame is pretty useless, except as an eventual motivator to relapse." ANONYMOUS

People trying to recover from an addiction are often given suggestions about things to avoid. "I just need to avoid pot!" you might say. Well, of course. But you've already decided to do that.

What you also need to be aware of are things that will make you more susceptible to moments of weakness. Everyone is tempted to relapse. You are no exception. It doesn't make you in any way a bad person. It makes you a human who is trying to make changes to his or her life. That is a wonderfully positive thing!

An important key in your recovery is minimizing moments of weakness, and making them less tempting. That's where the following list comes in very handy. It was derived from sources dealing with alcohol addiction, but the same principles apply to anyone trying to abstain from any addiction. Our reasons for any compulsive behavior are typically the same; therefore, the strategies used to avoid relapse easily overlap.

Exhaustion. Allowing yourself to become overly tired or in poor health. Some people, when quitting, might be prone to work addiction. Perhaps because they are in a hurry to make up for lost time. Maintaining good health and getting enough rest are important. If you feel good, you are more apt to think well. If you feel bad, then you might begin to think a "toke" won't make really make things any worse.

Dishonesty. Dishonesty begins with a pattern of little lies and deceits with fellow workers, friends, and family, followed by the lies to yourself. This is called rationalizing: making excuses for not doing what you should be doing, or for doing what you should not do.

Impatience. Things are not happening fast enough. People are not doing what they should be doing or what you want them to do. Impatience almost always leads to anger and frustration. Be careful.

Argumentativeness. Arguing small or unimportant points of view indicates a need to always be right, or in control. Loosen up! Don't sweat the small stuff. Sometimes we argue simply to look for an excuse to go back to smoking.

Depression. Unreasonable and unaccountable despair may occur in cycles and should be dealt with and talked about. Recovery requires a sense of hope. There are people in your life who want to help you cultivate that. If not, you can find some! They are as close as the nearest Marijuana Anonymous meeting.

Frustration. This includes frustration with people and frustration over things not going your way. Remember, not everything is going to go just the way you want it. This should not be used as another excuse to escape via smoking.

Self-Pity. Self-pity includes thoughts such as; "Why do these things happen to me?" or "Why must I be an addict?" or even "Nobody appreciates what I am doing (for them)." A great antidote to self-pity is thankfulness. See the Gratitude List on page 135 and add to the things you can be thankful for. If you can't list a hundred things, you're not trying hard enough.

Cockiness. The "I got it made" attitude of no longer fearing the addiction, or returning to drug situations to prove to others that there isn't a problem. Do this often enough, and it will wear down your defenses.

Complacency. Complacency and cockiness are sometimes linked. It is very dangerous to give up on your new disciplines simply because everything is going well. To always have a little fear or to be cautious is a good thing. Relapses often occur when things are going well.

Expecting too much from others. "I've changed, so why hasn't everyone else?" It's a plus if they do, but even if they don't, this is about you and your problem, not them. They may not even trust what you are saying yet. You can't expect others to change their lifestyles just because you have. You make the choices for your life; their choices don't control yours.

Letting Up on Disciplines. Prayer, meditation, yoga, daily inventory, diet, etc. are all methods people can use in recovery. Not using these can stem from complacency, boredom or cockiness. You cannot afford to be bored with your recovery. The cost of relapse is always too great.

Wanting Too Much. Do not set goals you cannot reach with your normal effort. Do not expect too much. It's always great when good things you weren't expecting actually happen. Hopefully, you will get what you deserve as long as you do your best, but maybe not as soon as you think it should happen. Happiness is not having what you want, but wanting what you have.

Forgetting Gratitude. You may be looking negatively at your life, concentrating on problems that still are not totally corrected. It is a good thing to remember where you started from and how much better life is now. Remember the list of things to be thankful for?

It Can't Happen to Me. This is dangerous thinking! Almost anything can happen to you, and it may, if you get careless. Remember, addiction is progressive, and you will be in worse shape if you relapse.

Omnipotence. This is a feeling that results from a combination of factors. You think you have all the answers for yourself and others. No one can tell you anything. You ignore any suggestions or advice. Relapse is probably imminent, unless a drastic change of attitude takes place.

This is a good list to review from time to time, just to keep these things in mind. You don't need to constantly think about it, but you do need to stay aware of these things. Pay attention to yourself. Keep tabs on your thoughts, your feelings, and especially your attitude. By being aware, you can choose to keep yourself moving in a positive direction.

The battle, I think, is wonderfully captured by this anonymous post, which I will quote in its entirety:

> *I haven't posted in while because I did give in. I went to a theme park with a bunch of smokers and I resisted it the whole day with that crowd. But, on my way home I made arrangements with my normal group of friends (knowing full well the implications), and ended up smoking with them. Then I smoked on Monday afternoon after watching a movie alone, and again on Monday night with my friends at poker.*
>
> *My friend then dumped his last bit of hash on me and I smoked half of it today and threw the rest away about 6 hours ago. Today, I've watched close to probably 8 hours of television and I have eaten a fair amount. I'm ashamed, and I feel like shit. I felt so much better when I was clean.*
>
> *Actually, sitting here writing this makes me think about weed, and I actually want to go and get some right now. If I analyze it for a second, it's like, "Why? What are you going to do once you're stoned? Watch more TV? Eat more? What's the freaking point?" I guess it will give me a buzz for maybe an hour, which I'm kind of craving now, but then I'll just be right back here again except feeling worse. Damn it, I don't know what to do with myself!* ANONYMOUS

This brilliantly portrays the cyclic nature of the smoking habit. We know the outcome, and many times we know the solution. How ironic that this poster's rollercoaster ride didn't really begin until after he left the theme park.

Let's try not to be too hard on ourselves. The majority of people reading this book have been in the same position as this guy, continuing to dangle on the fence of "abstinence" or "non-abstinence." The advantage that you and this poster have is the desire to quit. This puts you light-years ahead of millions of smokers.

However, if your desire is intact, I am not implying that it would be prudent for you to call your supplier, or start digging through your old hiding places for any leftover remnants. Otherwise, you will experience the same agony this poster was going through. Furthermore, you will probably have to begin this process over again. In many cases, this won't happen until you have become so miserable with yourself that you build up the determination to try this feat once again.

The point is that you have to understand the cyclic thinking of smokers. When you truly understand this, you realize you have to stay alert and serious. Serious means getting rid of those things in your life that tempt you, including the people, places, and things that are a bad influence. Temptations will come, even months afterwards. And especially when you're cocky enough to think you have defeated the addiction.

Trust me when I say that you do get better and more resilient with each cycle. Your reasoning becomes more absolute and the deceptions about the habit become more evident. Obviously, some of us ride the merry-go-round more than others before we decide to get off and see the world while it is not spinning. It is a cycle, but a cycle that can end with a true persistence to regain what you know is the right way to live.

CHAPTER 17

Relationships

Relationship issues present their own set of challenges when you are in the process of making major changes to your life. This isn't just true about quitting smoking, but it is certainly very true in this case. I touch on some of these challenges in other places in the book, but I want to highlight two here: deciding which relationships you need to discontinue, or at least take a break from, to accomplish your goal, and deciding who to tell what concerning your decision.

Deciding Who to Hang Around

"Courage does not always roar; sometimes courage is the quiet voice at the end of the day saying, "I will try again tomorrow."

MARY ANNE RADMACHER

Often breaking an addiction entails making tough decisions, and many times that means separating yourself from people very close to you. The people I smoked with the most often were family. Obviously, I couldn't just give them up like the pot! But I did make it a point to stay clear as much as possible, particularly in the beginning. There just always seems to be that good reason to concede lurking around the corner.

When breaking an addiction, there really is no one set plan of attack that works universally for everyone. Each person has different motivations, circumstances, history, and so forth. It isn't until after a number of trials-and-failures that most people discover what works best for them. However, being involved with your pot-smoking friends, while quitting, is a recipe for failure.

After the body gets used to living without pot, you still have to deal with established mental patterns or habits. Chronic smokers can easily fall back into the habit after the pledge not to smoke has been broken. After one smoke, you have given yourself permission to have another and, slowly, the habit can creep back into your life.

However, one thing is definite. If you resume smoking, *everything* will go exactly back to the way it was, and then the cycle of "smoke-guilt-quit-suffer-smoke" begins again. Many smokers have gone through this many times. Do you see yourself smoking for the next twenty or thirty years? Hopefully not, but the fact of the matter is we all thought that at one time. Then year after year, cycle after cycle, you continue to smoke.

I don't think you are necessarily naïve or foolish for trying this while keeping your friends. Many of us have tried to maintain unhealthy relationships while trying to quit. However, there has to be some real change or motivation for you to succeed with this approach. Do what you feel you need to do. If you fail, at least you will know next time what not to do.

I read something that reminded me of how influential the people in our lives are, for good or bad. It said that "if we hang out with losers, we gravitate toward losing, and if we hang out with winners, we gravitate toward winning. The reason is simple; we either cooperate or compete with the people in "our environment." That's something to think about.

Many of us fear the thought of being alone through this process, especially since many of our companions are friends we have accumulated through smoking. However, you need to let go of that fear. You will not be alone, because you will begin to attract the right kind of people into your life to support you with your desire to change. As Coretta Scott King said, "When you are willing to make sacrifices for a great cause, you will never be alone." Open yourself up to allow the right people to come into your life.

Be Careful What You Say

"Weed . . . the magical plant that gives you answers without questions. It gives the ability to think and dream with one hand, and takes away ambition and want with the other."
ANONYMOUS

Be careful of what you say, or promise. Life has a funny way of challenging us. Not to maliciously prove us wrong, but to see if we truly mean what we say.

I distinctly remember standing in front of the restroom mirror at work, during one of my many attempts at quitting. It had been two weeks, the amount of time it takes for many of us to start getting a little cocky, as if we have already succeeded.

But, of course, I felt this time was different. Feeling a deep remorse about being so disconnected from my two-year-old son because of my neglect, and the sense that I had a new lease on life, I looked into the mirror and with deep emotion I boldly proclaimed, "I would rather die from the stress than to smoke again!"

Well, "life" did it again. It wasn't one week later that a circumstance arose at work that I literally thought was going to kill me, because of the stress. Obviously, this probably wasn't the case, but my ability to cope had been seriously impeded by smoking for years. My body was screaming at me, "I can't handle this! Let's go to the garage and get away from this mess!"

How many times during an attempt at quitting have you told those close to you that this time was different? If it's not about smoking, it's about a girlfriend or boyfriend. We tell all of our friends that it is over this time, and that you're moving on for real.

But, just like the other 21 times you said that, they find you the following day snuggling in each other's arms again.

Isn't smoking the same way? You adamantly inform those close to you about your plans to stop, and then you find yourself having to hide it from them, until they find you cuddling with each other again.

As I was reading through many of the posts online, I noticed a common trend among the quitters who were giving advice. On average, these individuals had only been abstinent for about three to four weeks. Many of them spoke of their addiction in past terms, as if they had already defeated the problem, and were ready to save the rest of the world from their captivity to weed.

How come we don't have the people who have been clean for one or two years giving advice? It's probably because there aren't many of them around. Don't forget that the failure rate of abstinence from other drugs doesn't even come close to the failure rate from marijuana. I know you want to declare to the world that you have finally defeated your crutch. But the true measure of a person's success is not by what is proclaimed, but rather by what is done. Most successful people don't feel the need to proclaim their accomplishments to the rest of the world. Their actions and accomplishments speak for themselves.

Now, I am not saying that you do not need a support team. This is an extremely important component. However, the team should be more like the size of a bobsled team, not the size of a football team.

Let your actions speak louder than your words. More than likely, there are people around you who have heard these words before. As the Nike slogan says, "Just Do It!" People will eventually make up their own minds about your commitment. True change in an individual needs no explanation. It is what it is.

CHAPTER 18

What About God?

It is for freedom that Christ has set us free.
Stand firm, then, and do not let yourselves be
burdened again by a yoke of slavery. . . . You,
my brothers, were called to be free. But do
not use your freedom to indulge the sinful
nature, rather, serve one another in love.

Galatians 5:1, 13

Since I was a young boy, I have always had difficulty with reli-
gion. Spending time in a charismatic Pentecostal church as a
child and watching scores of people receive something that was
an unidentifiable mystery to me initiated a lingering question of
whether God even existed. I was only five years old at the time.
Besides, my nature has always been one of questioning the reality
of things, not just the existence of a higher power.

I have always been prone to skepticism. So much so that, before
I could read, I can even remember thinking that people were just
making things up when they were reading aloud. Obviously, this
started at a very young age. So, you can see how difficult it was for
me to understand or believe in something that I could not touch,
or observe. At least with the material that was being read, I could
see the words, and the piece of paper it was written on.

This questioning continued into my early twenties. In fact, it was a dominate part of my life, as I struggled concerning belief in the existence of God. My biggest fear was to die and not be given the opportunity to know the truth. If the existence of God was true, and I didn't believe, then the threat of being tossed into a fiery hell was horrifying. It just didn't seem fair. Besides, I was a good kid, for the most part.

Then a tragedy occurred in my life that was beyond my comprehension. After so many years of searching and being afraid, I was done. Why would this God, a so-called loving God that so many people dedicated their lives to, allow this misfortune to occur? As I lay in bed that night, I told God I was finished. Somehow, I missed the irony that I was informing God, who apparently didn't exist, that I didn't believe in him.

Nevertheless, I was serious. I was done. I had spent most of my life trying to believe in his existence and this is what I got in return? There was actually comfort in knowing that my search for an answer had finally ended.

Well, I don't think God took the matter lightly, and I came to realize that although I may have been done with God, he apparently wasn't done with me. Over the next few days my newfound understanding began to change.

I share this story with you so that you understand a little more about my faith. The questions have not stopped and the skeptical little boy still resides within me. But my belief in a higher power is concrete. After many years of trying to understand, I have concluded that I will never fully understand, and therefore, will never judge anyone else for their understanding. It's very simple. I do not judge Hindus, Muslims, or Jews for their beliefs. I do not judge people for their unbelief, either. We must all walk our own path in life.

However, I feel privileged to know and understand God through Jesus Christ. Most of my understanding comes through the teachings of the Bible that I have gathered through my own personal Bible reading. I have never taken the interpretations of other people's beliefs about Christianity or the Bible as absolute. I am not ashamed to tell others that I do not fully comprehend the relationship between the "Father and Son," for instance, or that I have difficulty interpreting the meaning of Christ's dying on the cross.

Nevertheless, a true understanding of Christianity came to me when reading the Gospel of John. I simply changed the word Jesus, Christ, etc., in the first few pages and replaced them with "Truth," "Love," and "Word." This made sense to me as to the universality of Christ without diminishing those who have not heard this message, yet practice this love every day of their lives.

So, how does all of this fit into resolving addictions of any kind? Many people attribute their success to God or Christ "lifting" this addiction or temptation off of them. The temptations were simply removed, so that they no longer suffered with the burden.

I believe that there are people that this happens to. However, I also believe that sometimes we see those individuals eventually traveling down the road of addiction again. On the other hand, there are many individuals who have recovered from an addiction without believing in God, and who have never returned to their addiction.

Many programs, such as Alcoholics Anonymous, place the belief in a higher power, God, as the centerpiece to recovery. There are other ministries that provide shelter and clothing to drug addicts who are homeless, while preaching them to recovery. Many of these addicts leave the homes and enter back into the streets, but only a few go on to lead normal, drug-free lives. Is it because "the God thing" doesn't work?

I don't think so. Rather, it has everything to do with the fact that we have been given free will to decide how to live our lives. For years I prayed for God to take away my dependency on marijuana. When I finally came to the realization that the work had to be done by me, I began to take on the responsibility to make that happen.

Every day of your life you are confronted with something that you probably know you shouldn't do. Ultimately the decision to do it, or to not do it, weighs on you, not God.

Nonetheless, for me personally, it was the belief in the teachings of my faith, and my desire to do right in the eyes of God, which played a major role in my persistence to overcome this habit. Through all of the unsuccessful attempts, the desire to overcome it never left.

Sometimes we question why we go through things in life without knowing that they play a greater purpose in our lives. I, too, questioned, pleaded, and prayed to God to remove what I felt at the time had so much control over me. Many of us pray for God to give us the strength to overcome these things, but we need to realize that much of the strength needs to come from within us. God simply provides that longing in us to be better examples of the Truth.

As I said, many people overcome their addictions without even acknowledging the existence of God. But, in most cases, these people did it for something or someone else. They did it for some unselfish reason in order to be a better person. I firmly believe that there is an inherent good in all people waiting to surface. Whether we know it or not, we are all just trying to please the innate nature of God that resides within each of us. Even if that little skeptical child resides within you, I am sure you will find the strength necessary to finish what you have started.

> "Keep on asking, and you will be given what you ask for. Keep on looking, and you will find. Keep on knocking, and the door will be opened. For everyone who asks, receives. Everyone who seeks, finds. And the door is opened to everyone who knocks." MATTHEW 7:7-8

CHAPTER 19

One Month: The Defining Point

The cold sweats, the funky dreams, the insomnia, the pit of depression I inhabited for the first few weeks, the loss of appetite—these all seem like a distant dream now and I have to think back to remember how I felt in those moments. It was all temporary and the feelings passed on by. Leaving me with that gift we call clarity of mind.

Anonymous

For some reason, the one-month mark is a defining point. I remember the little incremental steps, which felt like milestones at the time. The milestone of the first day, then the first week, and then the *big one* . . . the one-month mark! Well, they actually are *huge* milestones. It's just that soon they will be a distant memory for you, and will seem much smaller in the grand scheme of things to come. Before long, it will be just an accumulation of time that you periodically reflect on, grateful for how much progress you have made.

By now, many of those nasty withdrawal symptoms you experienced in the first week or so are gone. There is no more drenching your sheets from the intense nighttime sweating. And what about the irritability issues when you were acting out like a baby who couldn't get a toy it wants to play with? Looking back, that's really what the irritability and anxiousness was all about. Weren't we just throwing grown-up temper tantrums because we couldn't get what we wanted? Now it seems a little silly, doesn't it?

Some of you might still be experiencing intense dreams from time to time, but for the most part, these have subsided, or at least have become more enjoyable. Isn't it nice to be able dream normally again? To actually remember a dream, even a pleasant one, is one of those small things you can appreciate about your accomplishment. Another one is the fact you are probably able to sleep as your body was designed to do. I say "probably" because so many people have sleep problems due to other reasons. But most of you should be sleeping well and waking up refreshed and not groggy from the mountain of food you piled in your gut the night before.

You are to be congratulated on the accomplishments or changes you have made in your personal or professional life in only one month. Also, congratulations on the failures or stresses you have had in your personal or professional life in the previous one month. That comment may sound impractical, but the fact that you are living and experiencing life as everyone else does is great!

Many of you have seen things naturally change for the better. Whether you are thinking more clearly, communicating better, socializing more, or loving more, you are a different you. I guess I should say the "real you."

Some of these positive changes have taken a little more effort, because there were problems that you needed to work on which were present even before the smoking habit. Obviously, to expect these to be eliminated in one month would be naïve. So, keep working toward eliminating them. At least you now have the capacity to put forth the effort without the constant sleepwalking through life.

As far as overcoming those unpleasant situations, you've done a great job! You have succeeded in working through a problem, or are working through one, and you haven't succumbed to your old way of coping. Prior to this point, you have used marijuana to cope with life. There is a big difference in coping with a situation versus managing the situation.

Before, when a difficult circumstance would arise, you would simply take a puff, sit back, and hope the problem would go away. With some problems you actually had to do something, but that something was possibly one step above nothing. No one ever said all of these challenges were easy to handle, but not complicating them with a lackadaisical effort, if any effort at all, will help you create a life with a different experience.

Are you actually feeling less dependent? Maybe you feel that you have finally taken back control of this habit. Be very careful with this thinking. I am not suggesting that this feeling is false or unreal. It is real. You *are* less reliant. Smoking does not have control of you like it did a mere four weeks ago. But this is the second most common point where many people relapse (the first week is the most common). Four weeks is not enough time for you to lose discipline. In fact, you should never lose discipline, although the discipline does take much less effort the farther you go.

Here's the problem: some of you may be getting a little confident, or worse yet, cocky, around the fourth week, and will begin skipping or eliminating various steps/actions that have gotten you to this point. Or, you are entertaining the illogical idea that it is time to "reward" yourself with a smoke because of your "good behavior." Remember to manage your thoughts! Don't go there.

Now is a good time to remember back to those other periods of "quitting" when you gained some confidence and thought you had enough control to smoke only one, or just occasionally. What happened then? Who was really in control?

For many of you, this is the longest period of abstinence in many years, and you are feeling a great sense of victory. And you should be proud. You should be very proud of yourself that you have accomplished something that the majority of smokers have never even attempted, or have failed miserably at trying. Do you know how many of these smokers wish they had accomplished what you have?

So be vigilant, stay with your program, and keep climbing upward!

PART IV
GETTING HEALTHY

CHAPTER 20

Enlisting Your Body's Help

To quit using marijuana, you have to confront your desire to get stoned. You will be going into battle against yourself that you no longer wish to exist. Giving up marijuana, especially if you've been using for some time, is a bit like losing an old friend. Quitting may feel like a funeral, but it is also the beginning of a new life.

Brief Counseling for Marijuana Dependence Manual

This is a part of the book that many of you will turn to early in the process of reading the book, and that is probably a good thing. Some of these suggestions are going to help you tremendously. The idea of just going "cold turkey" sounds pretty macho, but in reality, it's more like going to the battlefield wearing just your underwear. Besides, the recommendations in this chapter and the next are a great way to live your life anyway. You will think more clearly, have more energy, and just feel and look better. There's nothing wrong with that.

But there is one catch . . . you have to do the work.

The symptoms typically people experience from the withdrawals are very similar, give or take a few. Moreover, just because you get through the initial stages of abstinence, it doesn't mean you are "free and clear." The emotional drive to abstain that is present in the beginning does dissipate. Therefore, making the appropriate lifestyle changes during this time is vital.

As I've said, the success rate for people quitting marijuana and continuing their abstinence is lower than for any other drug, except for alcohol and cigarettes. So don't take these tips lightly. You're going to need them! And the truth is, they will change your life forever, and not only in regard to helping you quit marijuana. They will have many other positive benefits as well.

Get Your Body in Motion!

"Those who think they do not have time for bodily exercise will sooner or later have to find time for illness." EDWARD STANLEY

If you do a web search on exercise and drug addiction recovery, you will find exercise is a highly recommended method for not only assisting in the initial stages, but for maintaining long-term abstinence as well. As important as it may be, exercise might be the most difficult piece of advice for people to adhere to.

Some of you already have a consistent exercise regimen, or at least engage in some sort of physical activity. For many, this is new territory and might be more difficult to implement. Therefore, we will discuss some of the benefits of exercising during recovery, and give a few tips on getting a program going.

The most popular study on exercise and addiction was done by Bess Marcus of Brown University's Center for Behavioral and Preventive Medicine. The study evaluated the effects of exercise on 281 healthy but sedentary females who were trying to stop smoking cigarettes. For 12 weeks, all of the women in the study attended a weekly smoking-cessation program, but roughly half of the participants were enrolled in wellness classes three times a week, while the other half participated in supervised exercise sessions three times per week.

The basic outcome for the study was that the women who participated in the exercise program were twice as likely to become and remain smoke-free, compared to the women who attended the wellness classes but did not exercise. Furthermore, the percentages were best among those who had attended the greatest number of workouts.

In a Brown University News Bureau release, Marcus said that regular activity offered a wealth of benefits for individuals who were attempting to kick an addiction. "There are numerous health benefits to participating in an exercise program," she said. "For starters, exercise helps you manage weight, stress, mood, anxiety, and depression."

Exercise makes us feel good about ourselves because of the impact it has on increasing dopamine, the so-called "feel good" chemical in the brain. In most compulsive disorders, users are seeking to raise dopamine levels. If you are no longer stimulating the production of dopamine with marijuana, you are going to need ways to help boost your levels. This will help you avoid the mood problems people experience when going through withdrawal.

Another benefit to exercise is detoxification. Understandably, many people want to eliminate the many toxins that have accumulated throughout the years. Your body is an amazing machine that is designed to get rid of pollutants naturally, and exercise helps this process. In addition to increasing blood flow and lymph fluids, which are both responsible for removing toxins and other harmful materials, the increase in body temperature will induce more sweating. The skin is a major route of detoxification, and sweating is a great way to get toxins out of your system.

It is well known that THC, the most prevalent psychoactive chemical of marijuana, is stored in fatty tissue. This is one of the reasons marijuana will remain in your system longer than other drugs. As you exercise, your body will use this fat for energy, thereby reducing the amount of fatty tissue in the body. The less fat, the less THC floating around your system.

Finally, your lungs have taken a beating ever since you began this smoking habit. Many of you will continue to smoke cigarettes in the beginning, but whether you do or don't, everyone will benefit by removing the phlegm and tar buildup in one of your most precious organs. Phlegm and tar removal will happen naturally once the smoking ceases, but forcing the expansion and contraction of the lungs through exercise will get this out even faster.

Here are a few tips for you to start exercising. My thanks to my good friend and fitness guru Eddie Enriquez for some of the following. (You can find more ideas on exercise and nutritional programs on his website at www.mytrainer.com.)

- Low-to-moderate intensity exercise is more effective at raising dopamine levels than higher intensity exercise. The idea here is to get your body in motion, increase your heart rate, and sweat a little. Twenty to thirty minutes of moderate exercise will accomplish this. You don't have to go to a gym. Light jogging, brisk walking and even jumping on a mini-trampoline can do the trick. The most important thing is finding something you enjoy and then *doing it*!

- Follow the lead of a woman named Marsha Doble: "I have to exercise in the morning before my brain figures out what I'm doing." Exercising first thing in the morning will help increase dopamine levels in the brain for the remainder of the day. Making this effort first thing in the morning can result in reduced stress levels, significantly improved mood and more energy throughout the day.

- Aim to keep your heart rate between 60 and 80 percent of maximum while exercising. A simple way to figure your maximum heart rate is to subtract your age from 220. However, you should talk to your doctor about your personal maximum. According to a study conducted at the University of Pittsburgh and presented at the October 2009 meeting for the Society for Neuroscience, exercise that keeps your heart rate in that target range helps to boost dopamine production, and more importantly, protect the existing dopamine receptors in your brain from the effects of aging.

Can't I Just Take a Pill?

"The research to date suggests a common biological essence to all addictions . . . though I don't think we'll ever have a single magic bullet. We might instead one day have neurochemical cocktails that are specific to each addictive drug that would break the cycle of craving." ALAN LESHNER, DIRECTOR, NIDA

Can we just take a pill to solve our problem? Well, the answer is yes and no. There are aids that we can use to help us cope with the withdrawals and cravings of the drug. However, depending on a simple solution, such as a pill, will only get you so far.

Trying to overcome marijuana dependence without considering the societal, economic, and psychological factors contributing to why we smoke, and working to address those issues, is like trying to drive a car without any gas. You won't get very far.

The most important part of your recovery depends upon your participation. So the old adage "the buck stops here" comes into play. That's not something you can get out of a pill bottle. Having said that, there are some very exciting and worthwhile supplements you should consider taking while going through withdrawal. I will also list a few things that some people recommend but that I would avoid, either due to the side effects or because there are better alternatives. As for prescription medications, such as sleep aids and antidepressants, you need to discuss this with your personal physician.

This isn't an exhaustive list of things that could be recommended, but the following suggestions are the ones I feel are the most important, most effective, and most specific for marijuana smokers who are trying to quit. I know there are people who will resist these suggestions, but, as I have said before, you are going into battle, and it is always a good idea to have a little ammunition. Each of us is going to approach this in the way we believe is the most appropriate. However, after many failed and uncomfortable attempts to quit, using these recommendations helped me tremendously.

Amino Acids

Numerous studies and books have been written about the benefits of amino acid therapy. Amino acids have been shown to be beneficial for those with compulsive disorders associated with drug use or overeating. Even individuals with ADD/ADHD have benefited tremendously. Amino acid therapy is a powerful tool to use . . . if you understand how to use it properly.

Amino acid therapy works by helping restore neurotransmitter deficiencies in the brain. We looked at the issue of neurotransmitter deficiencies in Chapter 10, "The Dopamine Reward System," where we examined the theory of Reward Deficiency Syndrome postulated by Kenneth Blum, Ph.D. Many others, such as Julia Ross, M.A., author of *The Mood Cure*, and Charles Gant, M.D., author of *End Your Addiction Now*, have written extensively about using amino acids to help restore neurotransmitter deficiencies, like dopamine and serotonin. Just hearing the word "dopamine" should grab your attention as to the potential importance of amino acid therapy.

In your brain and body, there is a vast network of nerves that all messages, from movement to mood, have to travel. These various messages travel from one nerve to another via neurotransmitters. Without these chemical messages from the neurotransmitters making it to their intended destination, you could not be happy, hungry, sleepy, or even angry!

Many neurotransmitters exist, but there are a few that garner most of the attention when dealing with addictions. These are serotonin, dopamine, GABA, norepinephrine, and endorphins. There are some companies that have attempted to create a "shotgun" approach to restoring the neurotransmitter imbalances or deficiencies by creating "one size fits all" supplements. I can tell you from personal experience that this approach will not work, and it can make some people very uncomfortable.

When I first learned about amino acid therapy, I started haphazardly taking anything that I read which could have an impact on the brain, and therefore, the addiction. As a result, I was taking things my body didn't need, and in dosages that were way too high. In my excitement I failed to do the proper study to fully understand the implications of using amino acids on the neurotransmitters. I guess you could say I put the cart before the horse. But, as a result, I almost got ran over by the horse!

You really can't blame me. My thinking at the time was that they are just amino acids, so they shouldn't have any detrimental effect. Besides, wouldn't I just "pee out" the excess that my body didn't use? Oh boy, was I wrong. I started consuming this stuff by the truck loads based upon a few articles I had found on the "therapeutic dosages." My brain went into a tailspin as a result. I couldn't think clearly, my heart was racing, and I couldn't sleep either.

One lesson I learned about this experience is that these things really do have an effect. The second lesson I learned was that I needed to do proper research about a topic before I used it on myself, or others!

My story is not to discourage anyone from using amino acids to balance neurotransmitters. They are very safe. The body naturally makes a number of these substances, and several are found in many of the foods we eat. Moreover, by using them appropriately, they can be a valuable asset to your success in conquering this habit. My problem was that I was taking some that my body didn't need, or that I was not deficient in. Furthermore, many of these amino acids have differing effects. Some are intended to keep you up and alert, while others are meant to keep you calm. Taking both at the same time, and in high dosages, can confuse the body, to say the least.

For instance, two amino acids, L-phenylalanine and L-tyrosine, both stimulate the neurotransmitter norepinephrine (formally known as nor-adrenaline). Most people know about adrenaline and therefore can understand why my heart was racing, and I couldn't sleep! Conversely, GABA, gamma-aminobutyric acid, basically "turns-off" excitatory chemicals, like adrenaline. Understanding which of these to use, and the proper dosages, is an important step in taking advantage of the benefits of amino acid therapy.

The Secret Addiction website (secretaddiction.org) provides additional help here. For our members on the Secret Addiction website, we have created step-by-step questionnaires and forms based upon the work of Julia Ross, M.A., and other experts in amino acid therapy to help guide you in the right direction. Also, the science and understanding of this field is rapidly advancing, and we regularly update the website with the latest, best infor-mation. There are also certain tests, such as urinalysis, that can be performed to further identify neurotransmitter deficiencies. After researching many of the companies offering urine testing, the website has information on what I believe are the most reliable tests on the market. Additionally, I always encourage the correla-tion of your symptoms before implementing any supplement to restore an identified neurotransmitter deficiency.

However, there is one amino acid that I have consistently recommended for anyone going through the initial stages of withdrawal—5-hydroxy tryptophan, or 5-HTP for short. 5-HTP has already been mentioned in Chapter 14, but it is definitely worth mentioning it again. 5-HTP is a naturally occurring amino acid that is an intermediate step in the production of tryptophan to serotonin.

Serotonin is the neurotransmitter that is involved in mood, appetite, and sleep (serotonin can convert to melatonin). These are all affected when we are going through withdrawal. There is some speculation as to whether serotonin is even affected by chronic smoking. Some say it only affects dopamine (the pleasure/reward neurotransmitter).

The cannabinoid receptor system, ultimately responsible for these effects, was only discovered in 1990. It is not well understood, and given that the brain is loaded with cannabinoid receptors, it is very plausible that weed can have an impact, directly or indirectly, on the production of serotonin, and consequently leave you with a shortage as you start to withdraw.

The symptoms of withdrawal alone make it worthwhile to take this amino acid. Assuming that there is a shortage of the neu-rotransmitter that is responsible for mood, appetite, and sleep, including the one for pleasure (dopamine), you can potentially be left feeling terrible during the beginning stages of withdrawal. This is where 5-HTP can really help. The symptoms, such as depression, irritability, sleep deprivation, appetite problems, and the dreadful nightmares, can be greatly reduced by taking this supplement.

Many people ask about the safety of using 5-HTP. It is *very* safe, but the fact that it is "naturally" occurring in the body does not mean that you can eat it like candy. Keep in mind that this is what your body uses to produce serotonin, and is not the same as prescription anti-depressants.

Furthermore, 5-HTP does not flood the system with excess amounts of serotonin, but rather helps you produce enough to alleviate the problems. Many manufacturers instruct you to take 100 mg per day, but most of the literature has shown that taking 200 mg per day is most effective. I do not recommend taking this long-term, nor do you need to do so. Two months is long enough to assist you through the initial stages.

Vitamins and Minerals

A general increase in vitamin and mineral supplementation, along with a change in diet, is very helpful when abstaining from drugs. This just makes sense. Why would you want to be deficient in the very things that allow your body to function in the first place? Your immune system depends on vitamins. Your nervous system desperately needs adequate amounts of these. Vitamins also help detoxify your body. These are just a few reasons why vitamins/minerals are vital.

In general, heavy marijuana smokers have been shown to have very nutritionally deficient diets. On average, heavy users have higher cigarette-smoking rates and higher consumption of sodas and alcohol. Marijuana users also consume more sodium, fewer fruits, and more pork, cheese, and salty snacks.

Although the research is limited on the effect that marijuana has on the depletion of certain vitamins, most studies agree that vitamin C and carotenoids are depleted by smoking marijuana. Both of these substances are antioxidants that help protect you from toxins, such as marijuana smoke. As far as the common assumption that smoking depletes various B-vitamins, I couldn't find any good research to support this claim, especially concerning marijuana smoke.

However, there are still good reasons why you will need the B-vitamins while going through this process. There is no need to purchase them individually. A good broad-spectrum multi-vitamin and mineral complex is all you need. Many people will buy individual bottles of specific vitamins, but may miss out on others that they need.

Do not buy cheap! You do not necessarily have to buy the most expensive supplement, but you do need to know the quality of the company you are buying from. There are many inferior supplements on the market with inferior components. There is a reason why they are cheap. Furthermore, if you really want to save money on vitamins and supplements, then start eating the right foods suggested in the next chapter.

On the website I provide more guidance concerning where to purchase quality vitamins and supplements, but for now, let's review a couple of them.

Vitamin B – Many people consider B-vitamins as the "nerve vitamins" because these vitamins are involved in many processes related to proper nervous system function, such as your ability to handle stress. All B-vitamins are important, but the ones most often discussed are B5, B6, and B12, and folate (folic acid). B6 in particular is needed for the production of various neurotransmitters, previously discussed.

Vitamin C – Smokers, whether marijuana or cigarette, have below-normal levels of Vitamin C. Given that vitamin C is imperative for proper collagen formation, its depletion affects the skin of long-time smokers. Vitamin C's other two common benefits are related to antioxidant and immune system properties. It has many other functions as well. One thing is for sure—you do not want to go without this vitamin.

N-Acetyl Cysteine (NAC)

This supplement ranks pretty high on the scale of importance. In fact, it runs a close second behind 5-HTP. Why? N-acetyl cysteine (NAC) is an altered form of the amino acid cysteine. Although cysteine is found in high-protein foods, NAC is not. It is produced by the body. I have been prescribing NAC for years to my patients for three reasons: it is a great antioxidant, it helps boost immunity, and it works well at thinning mucus.

First, NAC helps synthesize glutathione, one of the body's most important natural antioxidants and detoxifiers. Virtually every cell requires glutathione for viability and function, with the liver and lungs being the primary sites of glutathione synthesis.

Furthermore, glutathione is known to aid in the transport of nutrients to two major classes of immune cells, therefore help-ing boost immunity. While purified glutathione is available as a dietary supplement, absorption is low. N-acetyl cysteine is thought to be a better method of boosting cellular glutathione levels.

Probably the most important benefit of NAC for smokers is its anti-mucosal properties. Just about everyone I know who quits smoking, whether it is marijuana or cigarettes, wants to eliminate excess mucus or phlegm from their body as soon as possible. NAC, by changing the structure of mucus, thins the phlegm trapped deep inside your lungs. I routinely prescribe this to my patients suffering with other conditions, such as bronchitis and flu, but it is definitely going to help you during withdrawal.

The amount you should take is 1200 mg per day. You can usually find NAC in 600 mg tablets. You should take this for the first three months of abstinence. When taken over an extended period, NAC can increase the excretion of zinc and other essential minerals, so you don't want to take it forever. This is another reason why you also need to supplement with a good multi-vitamin and mineral complex.

Essential Fatty Acids

Just about everyone has heard about the benefits of taking omega-3 fatty acids, or for short, fish oil. Another name that you will see is "EPA/DHA." The human body requires regular, ample omega-3 fatty acids to function properly. Many health experts and research-ers believe that omega-3 fatty acids are the one essential nutrient missing most in our modern-day diet. I agree. This deficiency is believed to play a major role in the prevalence of heart disease, cancers, and brain disorders.

Deficiencies in omega-3 fats have been linked to: depression, anxiety, mood swings, bipolar disorder, ADHD and ADD. If you notice, these are some of the reasons why people smoke marijuana in the first place. Researchers from institutions such as the Harvard School of Public Health have shown these conditions will greatly improve with increased omega-3 fatty acid intake. The bottom line is that fish oil is not only good for the body, but it is great for the brain. Even if you don't suffer with any of these conditions, other studies have shown memory and focus can improve with consistent use of fish oil supplements.

So, how much is enough? My opinion is that most people are taking too little fish oil. Given that most fish oil comes in 1000 mg capsules, that is the amount typically taken. However, research indicates the benefits derived from fish oil supplements are more impressive with dosages in the 3000 to 4000 mg range. Multiple sclerosis patients benefit from amounts as high as 10,000 mg. Obviously, you will not have to take that high of a dosage, but I would stay within the 3000 to 4000 mg range.

In addition, quality is especially important with fish oil. Poor quality fish oils (i.e., cheap) may contain many of the pollutants that have accumulated in our fish, such as PCBs, lead, and mercury. If it doesn't say "molecularly distilled," don't buy it. Molecular distillation allows the oils to be separated from the bad contaminants.

Things to Avoid

Several supposed "helps" are things I actually recommend that you *not* use as part of your program.

Detoxification Supplements – A big question during withdrawal is whether to detox or not to detox. The fact is your body will detoxify itself anyway. It always has and it always will. Although I have mentioned it before, I will say it again. You do not need to use detoxification supplements. If you choose to do so, that is fine. But it is not necessary. If you do all of the things I have asked you to do, such as the exercise, diet recommendations, and the supplement regimen, your body is going to be a detoxifying machine. This more natural approach is very effective and will not flood the system with toxins, causing you to experience more symptoms than just the typical withdrawals. Let's face it, most of us have a lot of "gunk" built up in our bodies other than just the marijuana, and you really want to get rid of this stuff in a more natural and slower way.

Detoxification kits and programs are very common today. These may be beneficial for eliminating the toxins that accumulate daily that are deeply embedded within our tissues. However, there has been some research on the subject of "reintoxification" and the possibility of increasing the cravings by the release of THC back into the system from the fat cells (Gunasekaran et al., 2009). I think the best course is to let your body naturally detoxify.

Melatonin – Melatonin is a supplement that I hear some people recommending for sleep disturbances. However, melatonin can have some pretty nasty side effects even though it carries a "natural" label. Yes, melatonin is a naturally occurring hormone produced by your pineal gland that is responsible for your body's sleep patterns and rhythms. But, don't let that fool you. This stuff can really throw your body's natural rhythms out of whack.

Melatonin has been used for treating insomnia, jet-lag and other sleep disorders by readjusting the body's biological clock. However, the side effects, which are common, include headaches, nausea, depression, nightmares and vivid dreams, irritability, abdominal cramps and dizziness. Those are the very things you are trying to avoid while going through initial withdrawal.

Furthermore, no one really knows what an adequate dosage amount should be. When melatonin was first introduced, the amounts recommended were very high. Even today you will find dosage recommendations ranging from .1mg up to 10mg. So, from the lowest to the highest recommendation is a factor of 100. Can you imagine me giving you this broad of a range for something like vitamin C, telling you to take somewhere between 500 and 50,000 mg? You would rightly assume that I have no idea how much you should take. Instead of taking melatonin, you are much better off using 5-HTP like I recommended.

Prescription Medication – I know I will possibly step on a few toes with this one, but I am not saying that prescription medications do not have their place. It's just that too many people are conditioned to run to their physician for a complicated, side-effect laden, and often less effective drug simply because it is packaged nicely and only available through a prescription.

Although there are some individuals who will need the help of a physician to assist them through severe cases of depression and other psychological disorders, most do not. I encourage anyone who is truly in need of prescription medication to not do this alone. There are issues that are imperative for you to address, and smoking might just be the "side-effect" of a more pressing and underlying condition.

However, for the vast majority of people, there is no need to use prescription drugs when many of the solutions are clearly laid out for you in this book. They are safer, more effective, and longer lasting.

You Are What You Eat

You may have heard someone say, "Your body is a temple, so keep it holy." That idea comes from a Bible verse (1 Corinthians 3:16-17), and that quote is actually taken a bit out of context, but the idea is a very good one. Our bodies house something precious—us—and we should keep them holy. "Holy" simply means set apart for something. We should make sure our bodies are "set apart" for what they were designed to do. They were designed to enable us to live worthwhile lives on planet earth. They weren't designed to be high all the time! That's not what they are for.

Having our bodies be set apart for what they are designed for means taking care of them. That means, first, not abusing them with the wrong substances. And that means providing them with the healthy substances they do need.

Obviously, this is not a book on eating right, or dieting, but one study showed that heavy marijuana users consume 41% more calories than non-users (Smit et al., 2001). Additionally, the foods you consume can have a significant impact on the success and ease of your recovery. I mentioned earlier that getting your body in motion was the most difficult thing to get people to do. Well, welcome to the second most difficult.

Getting people to change their eating habits is like asking them to jump out of an airplane with no parachute. Why? It's simple . . . we *love* food. Not just food, but great tasting food. Our entire lives, in most cases, revolve around eating. Many of our social interactions with family and friends, business lunches, romantic dinners, etc. have food as an essential centerpiece. Many of the same "feel good" chemicals that are produced in the brain, when you smoke, are also created when you consume the foods you desire. Unfortunately, many of these foods are the ones high in fat and sugar, which lack many of the nutrients your body needs during the process of quitting smoking.

The problem with most of us when we are choosing what to eat is that we only consider two things: does it taste good and will it satisfy my hunger? It's not a crime to want your food to taste good, and it defeats the purpose of eating if it doesn't satisfy your hunger. However, adding another question to those two will help you make better decisions before putting food into your mouth: what is this doing for my health? More importantly at this stage in your life, how is this food affecting my recovery? Believe it or not, your decisions about what you eat can affect your overall success, or failure, with abstinence.

We could devote an entire book to the concept of eating properly, but for the purpose of this book, we need to stick to the basic benefits of eating properly while going through recovery. The Secret Addiction website contains much more information pertaining to proper diets than I am able to put in one chapter. Furthermore, some of you may be vegetarians, which will require further knowledge of proteins, and their amino acids, to make sure you are getting the necessary combinations in the foods you eat. For now, let's just cover the basics.

Protein

Getting adequate protein is going to be one of the most important aspects of your diet. The main reason is because you will need many of the essential amino acids that most protein sources contain. Some proteins, like meats (fish, poultry, eggs, and meats) contain all of the essential amino acids (the ones your body cannot produce on its own), so these are termed complete. Incomplete proteins are the ones that contain some of the essential amino acids, but not all. Examples of these are grains, legumes, nuts, seeds, and certain vegetables.

Earlier in this chapter, I discussed amino acids in detail, and their important function of creating necessary neurotransmitters. Some amino acids also aid in the production of dopamine receptors. Not to belabor the point, but complete protein intake is a must when it comes to your diet. I have a concern for vegans who are not aware of this, and who inevitably do not get the proper combination of proteins. Fortunately, many of the incomplete protein sources can be combined to make a complete protein. (This is covered in detail on the Secret Addiction website.)

One last tip on eating meat: do not eat heavy meats before going to bed. By heavy meats, I mean the ones that are difficult to digest, like red meat. Intense "nightmarish" dreaming is part of this process that most people want to avoid, and eating heavy meats put such stress on the nervous and digestive systems that these alone can trigger bad dreams. Author Robert Brault put it humorously:

> Stored away in some brain cell is the image of a long-departed aunt you haven't thought of in 30 years. Stored away in another cell is the image of a pink pony stitched on your first set of baby pajamas. All it takes to get that aunt mounted on the back of that pony is to eat a hunk of meat loaf immediately before going to bed.

Fresh Fruits and Vegetables

It seems that no matter what fad diet we encounter, whether it is low fat, high protein, low carbohydrate, and all those in between, it always comes down to the amount of calories consumed, and eating fresh fruits and vegetables.

I have to stress the importance of "fresh," because getting proper nutritional benefits out of a can is nearly impossible. Not only have essential nutrients been processed out, but you may also be getting unnecessary sugars (high fructose corn syrup), which can hurt your recovery. "Real and Raw" should be the motto when choosing fruits and vegetables.

It's hard to argue with the health benefits of a diet rich in fruits and vegetables: lower blood pressure, reduced risk of heart disease, stroke, and various cancers; lower risk of eye and digestive problems; and a mellowing effect on blood sugar that can help keep appetite in check.

Also, eating fresh fruits and vegetables helps detoxification, raises dopamine levels, and controls insulin levels. Fresh fruits and vegetables contain all of the necessary vitamins, minerals, and enzymes your body needs to function properly. To ask your body to operate properly without these nutrients is like trying to turn on a lamp without electricity. Each fruit or vegetable contains an abundance of one or more of these nutrients, which is why you should choose a variety of colors: dark green, yellow, orange, and red.

Antioxidants are another vital component of fruits and vegetables. Antioxidants are the substances that essentially "pick up the trash" (free radicals) left over from various pollutants created inside or outside of the body. Smoke is one of the pollutants known to cause free radical damage to the cells of your body. We have all seen the effects that long-term cigarette smoking can have on the skin of the smoker. This damage not only occurs on the surface, but in every single cell of your body.

Avoid High Sugar Diets

You will notice that many strategies we have previously discussed revolve around dopamine production/processing and detoxification. Now we add the insulin factor.

For every marijuana addict, I would suspect there are at least a hundred sugar addicts. Even that may be an understatement. A vast number of people worldwide have full blown diabetes and millions more have the beginning stages of diabetes, called insulin resistance.

Most marijuana recovery programs suggest diets that are low in sugar, or refined carbohydrates. Nevertheless, it is rarely explained why this is recommended, other than the fact that keeping blood sugar levels well maintained will help control spikes in insulin.

Some have theorized that all drug addictions have an underlying connection to hypoglycemia, or insulin resistance. Personally, I believe tying any addiction to one mitigating factor limits proper care, and ignores other factors involved in human behavior. But the idea of hypoglycemia and its contribution to addiction is very plausible.

Whether or not that is technically true, insulin levels absolutely need to be kept in check. We are beginning to understand the role insulin plays in overall eating habits and brain chemistry, and not just its ability to control blood sugar levels. Ongoing research by Kevin Niswender, M.D., Ph.D. and Aurelio Galli, M.D., Ph.D. clearly shows the impact that insulin resistance has on creating neurotransmitter imbalances, in particular dopamine. *Stabilizing insulin spikes that are caused by a diet saturated with sugary and other high-carbohydrate foods is essential.* Anyone trying to quit marijuana but turning to high-carbohydrate foods instead is working at cross-purposes against their own body. Your body craves nutrition that will help it get back in balance, not take it more out of balance.

Proper Fluid Intake

We have all been told dozens of times to drink more water. The truth is that this actually is important when it comes to withdrawal, because of the need to detoxify. Getting the proper amount of fluids allows you to flush the body free of toxins. Most people do not take in nearly enough water to accomplish this; rather, we live in a constant state of dehydration. Proper hydration is absolutely vital to your body's ability to function efficiently, or to function at all. Every single cell in your body requires hydration to do its job properly. Furthermore, organs such as the gastrointestinal tract require adequate amounts of fluid. The gastrointestinal tract, or your bowels, is another major route of detoxification. "Dilution is the solution to pollution" is still one of my favorite detoxification sayings.

It is not necessary to get into the discussion of tap water versus bottled water. Most of you reading this book probably have access to both. Just drink it. As long as you don't get it from an unclean source, I am sure you will be fine. How much water you should drink is debatable. Some have recommended drinking half your body weight in ounces. So, if you are 200 pounds than drinking 100 ounces or approximately 10 full glasses would be appropriate. However, it is demanding to drink that amount consistently. A simpler method is to always have water accessible, and drink it. Besides, aren't our bodies intelligent enough to notify us when we need fluids through our thirst? We just need to replace the soda pop and other drinks with water.

A Final Note

Change is usually uncomfortable, and making changes in our eating is especially difficult. It has always amazed me to encounter those unique individuals who don't seem to have the passion for food that most of us share. As I said before, certain foods tickle the same areas of the brain that substances of abuse activate. However, it's time for you to make the necessary changes in your diet or, at least, start adding a few of the suggestions that are in this chapter. You don't need to be a fanatic. You can still enjoy your favorite foods. I have always used the ratio of 80% good and 20% bad. This will allow you to satisfy certain cravings without going overboard.

CHAPTER 21

Other Important Helps

When you can truly experience how a habit is
damaging what is most important to you, the steps
out of your destructive habit often fall readily into place.

Stanton Peele, Ph.D., J.D., *7 Tools to Beat Addiction*

I n this chapter I want to discuss some things that aren't cures for
addiction, but that can be a big help as you end yours. They are
great adjuncts to utilize during the various phases of recovery. You
will notice that the first three (chiropractic care, acupuncture, and
massage) all impact the "feel-good" chemicals in the brain. There
is nothing that replaces your desire to quit. Nevertheless, these can
make the ride much more comfortable. If you have access, *use them.*

Chiropractic Care

Chiropractic and addiction? Yes! A program in Miami is touting
some of the best success rates in the country with a holistic approach
utilizing chiropractic, acupuncture, and amino acid therapy.

But what does the spine have to do with addiction? The
connection may be explained by the presence, or absence, of neurotransmitters. When the spinal cord and its nerves are in proper
order, neurotransmitters are released in a specific sequence, like

falling dominoes. The result is a state of well-being. However, sub-luxations, or misalignments, of the spine can cause pressure and tension on surrounding tissue, interrupting this feel-good sequence.

Anyone who has gone to a chiropractor knows that after an adjustment, you definitely feel better emotionally than before. There is no doubt concerning the structural benefits to chiropractic care. But what most people don't realize is that chiropractic was not developed as an expensive treatment for headaches, or back pain. The originators of chiropractic recognized the relationship and impact that the spine has with the nervous system.

Given that the nervous system is controlling and regulating every process in your body, including the vital brain chemicals, it is essential while recovering from any addiction that this system operates free of any interference. Keep in mind that chiropractic does not treat any addiction, but should rather be used an adjunct to many of the other strategies listed in the book.

Acupuncture

Rehabilitation clinics and centers that specialize in Traditional Chinese Medicine (TCM) often use auricular acupuncture to treat addiction. This is a type of acupuncture focuses on acupoints in the ear.

Excellent clinical evidence supports the use of acupuncture for addiction control. Acupuncture is a natural procedure with no side effects, and it can treat a wide range of addictions. Addicts report a marked reduction in craving for drugs, a relief from symptoms of withdrawal, and feelings of relaxation along with improved sleep.

There is strong physiological evidence supporting the use of acupuncture in this area. Acupuncture has the effect of balancing neurotransmitters and stimulating the central nervous system, which ends up releasing "feel-good" chemicals in the brain, such as endorphins and serotonin. As we have seen, the cravings and withdrawal symptoms experienced by people giving up smoking or drugs can be mitigated by raising the level of endorphins in the nervous system.

Massage

Incorporating massage into a substance abuse program is advantageous in all stages of quitting an addiction: withdrawal, detoxification and abstinence. The physical, emotional and spiritual components of recovery all can be directly benefited by the healing power of therapeutic touch.

As with chiropractic and acupuncture, the primary reason massage is beneficial is because it affects the part of the brain that produces our "feel-good" chemicals, like dopamine and serotonin. This, in turn, reduces stress and tension.

The one advantage that massage has over chiropractic and acupuncture is that it can be done, to a degree, by a member in your own household. For example, even a five-minute neck and shoulder massage can relax you enough to prevent you from sneaking into your hiding place to "toke away" daily stresses. Although there isn't any comparison to a getting a professional massage, this can be very effective and I highly recommend it if you can arrange it.

Hypnosis

Hypnosis has become extremely popular lately as a complementary option for those undergoing treatment for marijuana addiction. The research indicates relatively high success rates when compared to other forms of treatment. Hypnotherapy can substantially affect your habits by routing messages straight to the subconscious. Most of our actions, or re-actions, are simply the brain on "automatic pilot."

Hypnosis can be tried in two ways. You can go to a hypnotherapist practitioner, or you can buy a CD, or mp3, that helps you with self-hypnosis in your own home. In the case of the CD, messages are woven into music of certain frequencies. If you visit a hypnotherapist, your sessions may be scheduled several times per week. On the other hand, a CD for self-hypnosis can be used multiple times per day, if you wish.

As always, I would not suggest that a CD is superior to the guidance of a competently trained hypnotherapist. It is, however, much more convenient.

Many hypnotherapists will themselves provide you with some form of audio as an adjunct to your clinical sessions. Either way, to actually benefit from hypnosis to treat marijuana addiction you must remain regular with your sessions. Most hypnosis treatments last for a couple of months. A minimum of 60-day usage is recommended with CDs for self-hypnosis.

After reviewing several companies that provide audio hypnosis for home use, one thing became very clear: be careful concerning the quality of the product you purchase. There are some very good hypnotherapy products on the market, and it's important to select a good one. I share with you my top picks on the Secret Addiction website. I highly recommend that you purchase a CD or mp3 to complement the other strategies in the book.

Visualization and Meditation

It would only be appropriate to follow hypnosis with information about visualization and meditation. The state of consciousness in meditation is often confused with hypnosis, but it is quite different. While both lead to an active process of thought, hypnosis is usually guided by another.

The literature on using meditation for addiction most often describes the Vipassana type of meditation. In Vipassana meditation, you don't try to deny or ignore thoughts related to addiction. Rather, when a thought or craving to use arises,

Vipassana meditation teaches you to observe and accept the presence of the thought while not over-identifying with it. In this way, you can acknowledge the reality of such thoughts while learning to refocus energy and intention elsewhere. This type of meditation is appealing to some because it avoids blame and stigmatization related to the addictive thought process, while also acknowledging its reality.

Vipassana meditation for addiction would begin with finding a quiet place without distractions and at least 20 to 30 minutes of dedicated time. While sitting in a chair or on the floor, you hold your head and back straight, in a comfortable position with eyes closed. This is a mindful form of meditation, with a focus on being aware of body sensations and thoughts. Therefore, if shifting or moving becomes necessary, it should be done with an awareness of the sensation and action of the movement.

The following is an example of a typical meditation session:

Relax, visualize the object of addiction; push it away, it is undesirable. Determine to be free from its power. Imagine cutting the strings of attachment, the emotional ties that bind. Walk toward the door, look back and know it's no longer needed. Now, go out the door, leave the house and go for a walk, feeling the freedom of leaving the object behind. Imagine this feeling lasting. Upon returning, the object is still there, but its appeal is lost.

Take longer walks around the neighborhood or the lake each time you practice this meditation, and finish the walk by disposing of the object in the garbage. Practice this visualization often, and as your determination to be free from its hold intensifies, the object will prove less appealing.

Meditation can take some practice to become efficient. Calming the excessive chatter in your mind can be more difficult than you think. If you are having difficulty, or prefer the idea of someone else guiding you through the process, then I recommend utilizing hypnosis. The mechanism of action is essentially the same, but listening to a guided session is usually easier, and it allows you to essentially "sit-back" and enjoy the ride. Once again, I suggest reviewing some of our recommended CDs or audio files on the website.

Drug Rehabilitation Centers

Drug rehabilitation centers can be a good source for those addicted to more common, and heavier, substances of abuse, such as alcohol, cocaine, and heroin. However, many centers are not equipped, or experienced, to properly manage marijuana addiction. Furthermore, it is a very expensive option for a drug that doesn't allow you to "hit rock-bottom" like other drugs.

I spoke with a mother who discovered her son was regularly smoking marijuana. Not knowing anything about the substance, she frantically called every drug rehabilitation center in her area to inquire about admitting her son for treatment. Believe or not, the majority of the centers she contacted either didn't have a program, or shrugged marijuana off as a non-addictive substance.

In fact, some programs encourage the use of marijuana as replacement for their primary substance of abuse. The common term for this is "marijuana maintenance." I will admit that marijuana in such cases is probably the lesser of two evils, at least for the moment. But I don't recommend substituting one unhealthy addiction for another.

Drug Counselors and Support Groups

In life, I am firm believer in having someone, such as a coach, mentor, or counselor, to help guide, recommend, and hold us accountable for our decisions. Throughout the book, I have cited the *Brief Counseling for Marijuana Dependence* manual. This manual was created for drug counselors to better prepare them for dealing with adults addicted to marijuana.

Just as *The Secret Addiction* is specifically aimed toward marijuana addiction, I would recommend finding a counselor who understands marijuana, and particularly one who has personally overcome the habit themselves. A simple online search will direct you toward counselors in your area. Local churches and governments are other good resources to use. Many times, drug counselors can be a less expensive option when utilizing their services outside of a rehabilitation center.

Support groups, such as Marijuana Anonymous, are another great resource. According to the Marijuana Anonymous website, the members are "a fellowship of men and women who share our experience, strength, and hope with each other that we may solve our common problem and help others to recover from marijuana addiction" (www.marijuana-anonymous.org). Support groups consist of people who have been down this road before. They understand what you are going through, and are there for you unselfishly without any cost. Support groups are everywhere. Your family and friends may know of some near you.

Blogging and Forums

Blogging and participating in online forums are excellent tools to use. No matter what time of day, or where you are in the world, someone is there waiting to support you. This tool can be extremely helpful during the beginning stages. The private nature of this resource allows you to be honest about your thoughts and experiences in a way that you may not feel comfortable with in another setting.

I can't stress enough to utilize online resources. The Secret Addiction website includes a free blog for you to share your experiences, and to give advice for those who are going through the same experiences as you. Our members who have "secret angel" status have completed their journey and are a great source of information and support. I have carefully selected the "secret angels" based upon their knowledge and understanding of this process. They are here for you.

PART V
A NEW FUTURE

CHAPTER 22

Writing the Final Chapter

If you want your life to be a magnificent story, then begin by realizing that you are the author and every day you have the opportunity to write a new page.

Mark Houlahan

So, here we are. The last chapter of the book. The final chapter of this story before moving on to another book. The new book—the story of your life, your future. This is it, or is it? For those of you who have traveled with me during the last month, and have succeeded, I commend you. But remember, this is only the beginning.

I have waited to write the final chapter. I knew that, if I was patient, the inspiration for the content would somehow appear. It did. And it is not just a strategy to overcome this one obstacle in your life. It is, in my opinion, how we achieve true greatness. Follow what I am about to write, and your life will be changed forever.

My first inspiration came after watching a program on four-star General Stanley A. McChrystal. Yes, there has been controversy surrounding General McChrystal since, but there is no denying the greatness of this person, and the dedication and discipline he maintains.

The program, which highlighted McChrystal's promptness, the fact that he sleeps a mere four hours per night, eats only one meal per day, and runs seven to eight miles every single day, left me with one thought: what are you willing to do to make a difference?

Think about that for a moment. I am more than certain that everything McChrystal does intentionally serves the function of making him a better leader, and a better soldier. Every decision he makes is ultimately linked to his purpose, or his mission. So, what are you willing to do to make a difference?

This leads me to my second inspiration. I had the unique opportunity recently to meet retired Brigadier General Rebecca S. Halstead. Not only is General Halstead a member of the first class of women to enroll at the United States Military Academy (West Point), but she is the first female graduate of West Point to attain general officer rank.

Do you think that a female who stands barely above five feet tall encountered any obstacles in her quest to lead a brigade of more than 20,000 soldiers in Afghanistan? When she speaks about leadership and obtaining success, I listen. You should too.

During our discussion, General Halstead shared with me two very important affirmations she read every day while in battle. The first, The Warrior Ethos, applies to our mission. Our mission, or our purpose, defines our actions, and the decisions we make. Live your life by applying this creed in everything you do, and it will change for the better.

> I will always place the mission first.
> I will never accept defeat.
> I will never quit.
> I will never leave a fallen comrade.

Do yourself a favor, and read that again. As far as your personal mission, pulling through this habit is only one part. It is a necessary part, however, in order for you to achieve "it." I am not sure what "it" is for you. "It" is different for all of us. But, by living in a cloud of smoke, I am certain you will never figure "it" out. The bigger the mission, the bigger you become.

The second affirmation given to me by General Halstead is a prayer. I wrote at the beginning of the book that God was very instrumental in my desire to continue with this journey. I hope that all of you can put religious dogma aside and make God a part of this process. The following prayer is a verse from the Bible, Joshua 1:9:

> Be strong and courageous.
> Do not be terrified;
> do not be discouraged,
> for the LORD your God
> will be with you wherever you go.

I can only imagine the meaning these must have had for General Halstead, while leading and protecting the lives of so many young soldiers in Afghanistan. If you only muster a fraction of the conviction she expressed when reciting these every morning, you can succeed at anything. It rises above the self-centered actions and motivations we usually exhibit, and diverts our attention to the betterment of those around us, and more importantly, our mission.

What are you willing to do to make a difference? If I leave you with anything, it would be that statement. Repeat it often. This has now become your battle. You are now a soldier in your own mission. Fight it with consistency, and endure the inherent discomforts that come with your decision. I wish you could fast-forward and see how great your life is going to be, now that you have decided to complete this chapter of your story.

Many decades pass by while some people continue to float on a cloud of mediocrity, seemingly content living a life of being high. But it's not true contentment. It's an illusion. It cannot possibly produce an individual who is able to look back and think, "I have lived well." Mel Gibson's character, William Wallace, put it succinctly in the movie *Braveheart*: "Every one of us will die. But so few of us really live." Do not let this happen to you.

I want to be one of the few who really live. Don't you?

References

Aldington S., Harwood M., Cox B., Weatherall M., Beckert L., Hansell A., Pritchard A., Robinson G., Beasley R., Cannabis use and risk of lung cancer: a case–control study, Eur Respir J 2008; 31: 280–286.

Aldington S, Williams M, Nowitz M, Weatherall M, Pritchard A, McNaughton A, Robinson G, Beasley R., Effects of cannabis on pulmonary structure, function and symptoms, Thorax. 2007 Dec; 62(12):1058-63.

Anthony JC, Warner LA, Kessler RC., Comparative epidemiology of dependence on tobacco, alcohol, controlled substances and inhalants. Basic findings from the National Co-morbidity Survey. Exp Clin Psychopharmacol 1994; 2: 244±68.

American Chemical Society (2009, June 15). Marijuana Damages DNA And May Cause Cancer, New Test Reveals. ScienceDaily. http://www.sciencedaily.com/releases/2009/06/090615095940.html

Bien T., Bien B. (2002). Mindful Recovery; A Spiritual Path to Healing form Addiction. New York: John Wiley & Sons, Inc.

Budney AJ, Hughes JR, Moore BA, Novy PL. Marijuana abstinence effects in marijuana smokers maintained in their home environment. Arch Gen Psychiatry 2001; 58:917–924.

Budney AJ, Moore BA, Vandrey RG, Hughes JR. The time course and significance of cannabis withdrawal. J Abnorm Psychol 2003;112:393–402.

Budney AJ, Novy P, Hughes JR. Marijuana withdrawal among adults seeking treatment for marijuana a dependence. Addiction 1999;94:1311–1322.

Carr, A. (2002). Easy Way to Stop Smoking. London, England: Arcturus Publishing Ltd.

Cohen, S. (1979). Marijuana: A new ball game? Drug Abuse and Alcoholism Newsletter, 8, 4.

DeFonseca FR, Carrera MRA, Navarro M, Koob GF, Weiss F. Activation of corticotropin-releasing factor in the limbic system during cannabinoid withdrawal. Science 1997; 276:2050–2054.

Donald P., Marijuana smoking - Possible cause of head and neck carcinoma in young patients, Otolaryngology - Head and Neck Surgery; Vol 94: 517-21 (April 1986).

Earlywine, M. (2002). Understanding marijuana; A new look at the scientific evidence. New York: Oxford University Press.

Edwards C. et al., Sensory Gating Impairments in Heavy Cannabis Users Are Associated With Altered Neural Oscillations. Behavioral Neuroscience. 2009, Vol. 123, No. 4, 894–904.

Eldreth DA, Matochik JA, Cadet JL, Bolla KI., Abnormal brain activity in prefrontal brain regions in abstinent marijuana users, Neuroimage. 2004 Nov; 23(3):914-20.

Filbey FM, Schacht JP, Myers US, Chavez RS, Hutchison KE., Marijuana craving in the brain, Proc Natl Acad Sci U S A. 2009 Aug 4; 106(31):13016-21.

Fried P, et al., Current and former marijuana use: preliminary findings of a longitudinal study of effects on IQ in young adults. CMAJ 2002;166(7):887-91.

Gant C., Lewis G. (2010). End Your Addiction Now; The Proven Nutritional Supplement Program That Can Set You Free. Garden City Park, NY: Square One Publishers.

Gieringer D., Marijuana Water Pipe and Vaporizer Study, Newsletter of the Multidisciplinary Association for Psychedelic Studies (MAPS). Volume 6 Number 3 Summer 1996 (revised 2000); http://www.maps.org/news-letters/v06n3/06359mj1.html

Grinspoon L., Bakalar J., Marijuana: The Forbidden Medicine. Yale University (1993).

Gruber SA, Rogowska J, Yurgelun-Todd DA., Altered affective response in marijuana smokers: An FMRI study. Drug Alcohol Depend. 2009 Aug 3.

Gunasekaran N, Long LE, Dawson BL, Hansen GH, Richardson DP, Li KM, Arnold JC, McGregor IS. Reintoxication: the release of fat-stored Delta(9)-tetrahydrocannabinol (THC) into blood is enhanced by food deprivation or ACTH exposure, Br J Pharmacol. 2009 Nov; 158(5):1330-7.

Haney M, Ward AS, Comer SD, Foltin RW, Fischman MW. Abstinence symptoms following smoked marijuana in humans. Psychopharmacology 1999;14:395–404.

Istvan Katona, Ede A. Rancz, Laszlo Acsady, Catherine Ledent, Ken Mackie, Norbert Hajos, and

Tamas F. Freund. Distribution of CB1 Cannabinoid Receptors in the Amygdala and their Role in the Control of GABAergic Transmission, The Journal of Neuroscience, December 1, 2001, 21(23):9506–9518.

Iversen, L., Cannabis and the Brain. (2003), 126, 1252±1270

Iyalomhe GB., Cannabis abuse and addiction: a contemporary literature review, Niger J Med. 2009 Apr-Jun;18(2):128-33.

Johnson, B. (2003). Psychological Addiction, Physical Addiction, Addictive Character, a nosology of addiction. Canadian J. Psychoanalytics, 11:135-160.

Johnston, LD.; O'Malley, PM.; Bachman, JG. Monitoring the Future National Results on Adolescent Drug Use: Overview of Key Findings. National Institute Drug Abuse; Bethesda, MD: 2000.

Kadden RM, Litt MD, Kabela-Cormier E, Petry NM., Increased drinking in a trial of treatments for marijuana dependence: Substance substitution? Drug Alcohol Depend. 2009 Jul 14.

Kouri EM, Pope HG. Abstinence symptoms during withdrawal from chronic marijuana use. Exp Clin Psychopharmacol 2000; 8:483–492.

Leshner A., Director, National Institute of Drug Abuse, National Institutes of Health, The Essence of Drug Addiction.

Leuchtenberger, Cecile and Rudolf, Cytological and cytochemical studies of the effects of fresh marihuana cigarette smoke on growth and DNA metabolism of animal and human lung cultures, The Pharmacology of Marihuana (Raven Press, New York 1976).

Lichtman AH, Martin BR. Marijuana withdrawal syndrome in the animal model. J Clin Pharmacol 2002;42:20S–27S.

Limperopoulos C, Soul JS, Gauvreau K, Huppi PS, Warfield SK, Bassan H, Robertson RL, Volpe JJ, du Plessis AJ., Late gestation cerebellar growth is rapid and impeded by premature birth, Pediatrics. 2005 Mar; 115(3):688-95.

Madrigal, A., December 22, 2008. "High Times in Ag Science: Marijuana More Potent Than Ever." http://www.wired.com/wiredscience/2008/12/high-times-in-a/

Mahmoud A. ElSohly, P. (2008). Quarterly Report, Potency Monitoring Project. Washington D.C.: University of Mississippi.

Marcus, B. H., Lewis, B. A., Hogan, J., King, T. K., Albrecht, A. E., Bock, B., Parisi, A. F., Niaura, R., & Abrams, D. B. (2005). The efficacy of moderate-intensity exercise as an aid for smoking cessation in women: A randomized controlled trial. Nicotine & Tobacco Research, 7(6), 871-880.

Markson, L. (2008). Talking to Yourself Is Not Crazy; Change Your Inner Dialog and Take Control of Your Life! Florida: SPS Publications.

McDonald, D.I. (1984). Drugs, Drinking, and Adolescents. Chicago: Year Book Publishers.

Mouslech Z, Valla V., Endocannabinoid System: An overview of its potential in current medical practice, Neuro Endocrinol Lett. 2009 Jun 13; 30(2).

Office of National Drug Control Policy. Teen Marijuana Use Worsens Depression, An Analysis of Recent Data Shows "Self-Medicating" Could Actually Make Things Worse. Rockville, MD: May 2008

Peele, S. (2004). 7 Tools to Beat Addiction. New York, NY: Three Rivers Press.

Peele, S. (1998). The Meaning of Addiction. San Francisco: Joey Bass.

Ross, J. (2002). The Mood Cure; The 4-Step Program to Take Charge of Your Emotions - Today. New York, NY: Penguin Group.

SAMHSA. Summary of Findings from the 2002 National Household Survey on Drug Abuse. USDHHS; Rockville, MD: 2003.

SAMHSA. Treatment Episode Data Set (TEDS) 1996–1999: National Admissions to Substance Abuse Treatment Services. DHHS; Rockville, MD: 2001.

Sarafian T. et al., Oxidative Stress Produced by Marijuana Smoke, An Adverse Effect Enhanced by Cannabinoids, Division of Pulmonary and Critical Care Medicine, Department of Medicine; and Division of Surgical Oncology, Department of Surgery, University of California at Los Angeles School of Medicine, Los Angeles, California, 1998.

Sharma, R. (2006). The Greatness Guide. Toronto, Ontario, Canada: HarperCollins Publishers, Ltd. Shiffman, S., "Coping with Temptations to Smoke," in S. Shiffman and T.A. Wills, eds. Coping and Substance Use (Orlando, FL: Academic Press, 1985), 223-42.

Singh et al., Evaluation of the DNA Damaging Potential of Cannabis Cigarette Smoke by the Determination of Acetaldehyde Derived N2-Ethyl-2'-deoxyguanosine Adducts. Chemical Research in Toxicology, 2009;

22 (6): 1181 Smiley, A. (1986). Marijuana: On-road and driving simulator studies. Alcohol, drugs, and driving, 2, 121-134.

Smit E., Crespo CJ, Dietary intake and nutritional status of US adult marijuana users: results from the Third National Health and Nutrition Examination Survey, Public Health Nutrition: 4(3), 781±786

Steinberg, K.L.; Roffman, R.A.; Carroll, K.M.; McRee, B.; Babor, T.F.; Miller, M.; Kadden, R.; Duresky, D.; and Stephens, R. Brief Counseling for Marijuana Dependence: A Manual for Treating Adults. DHHS Publication No. (SMA) 05-4022. Rockville, MD: Center for Substance Abuse Treatment, Substance Abuse and Mental Health Services Administration, 2005.

Stephens, R.S.; Roffman, R.A.; and Simpson, E.E. Adult marijuana users seeking treatment. Journal of Consulting and Clinical Psychology 61(6):1100–1104, 1993a.

Stephens, R.S.; Wertz, J.S.; and Roffman, R.A. Self-efficacy and marijuana cessation: A construct validity analysis. Journal of Consulting and Clinical Psychology 63(6):1022–1031, 1995.

Swift W, Hall W, Teesson M. Cannabis use and dependence among Australian adults: results from the National Survey of Mental Health and Wellbeing. Addiction 2001; 96: 737±48

Tashkin D. et al., "Effects of Habitual Use of Marijuana and/or Cocaine on the Lung," in Research Findings on Smoking of Abused Substances, NIDA Research Monograph 99 (1990).

Tashkin D., Is Frequent Marijuana Smoking Hazardous to Health?, Western Journal of Medicine 158 #6: 635-7 (June 1993).

Taylor DR, Fergusson DM, Milne BJ, Horwood LJ, Moffitt TE, Sears MR, Poulton R., A longitudinal study of the effects of tobacco and cannabis exposure on lung function in young adults, Addiction. 2002 Aug; 97(8):1055-61.

Taylor DR, Poulton R, Moffitt TE, Ramankutty P, Sears MR., The respiratory effects of cannabis dependence in young adults, Addiction. 2000 Nov; 95(11):1669-77.

Vandrey R., Budney A., Kamon J., and Stanger C., Cannabis withdrawal in adolescent treatment seekers, Drug Alcohol Depend. 2005 May 9; 78(2): 205–210.

Washton A., Boundy D. (1989). Willpower's Not Enough; Recovering from Addictions of Every Kind. New York, NY: HarperCollins Publishers.

Wu TC, Tashkin DP, Djahed B, Rose JE. Pulmonary hazards of smoking marijuana as compared with tobacco. N. Engl. J Med 1988; 318:347-51.

Young, S. October 16, 2007. "Tips for Breaking Bad Habits and Developing Good Habits." http://www.pickthebrain.com/blog/strategies-for-breaking -bad-habits-and-cultivating-good-ones/

Yücel, Murat et al., Regional Brain Abnormalities Associated With Long-term Heavy Cannabis Use, Arch Gen Psychiatry. 2008; 65(6):694-701.

Zimmer L., Morgan J. (1997). Marijuana Myths, Marijuana Facts; A Review of the Scientific Evidence. New York: Lindesmith Center.

Zhang Z., Morgenstern H., Spitz M., Tashkin D., Yu G., Marshall J., Hsu T., Schantz S., Marijuana Use and Increased Risk of Squamous Cell Carcinoma of the Head and Neck. Cancer Epidemiology, Biomarkers & Prevention. December 1999; Vol. 8, 1071–1078.

About the Author

Tony DeRamus is the CEO of SMA International, a company devoted to addressing the rampant abuse of marijuana worldwide by training, coaching and educating counselors and users through various mediums such as books, internet, and seminars. He also owns and operates one of the largest chiropractic clinics in North America. Dr. DeRamus has devoted his life to helping others achieve personal success in both life, and their health and well-being.

For additional resources on overcoming marijuana addiction, visit www.secretaddiction.org

Made in the USA
Las Vegas, NV
27 February 2023

68247525R00144